MW00625821

Posttraumatic Stress Disorder in Firefighters
The Calls That Stick with You

Paul J. Antonellis, Jr., MA, CEAP, CAS
Shannon Gwin Mitchell, PhD

CHEVRON
PUBLISHING CORPORATION

Printed in the United States of America

ISBN: 1-883581-26-5

Cover photo by Paul J. Antonellis, Jr.

CHEVRON
PUBLISHING CORPORATION

5018 Dorsey Hall Drive, Suite 104
Ellicott City, MD 21042 USA
Telephone: (410) 740-0065
Fax: (410) 740-9213

office@chevronpublishing.com

This book is dedicated to the three men whose stories you are about to read. With bravery they did their jobs and with bravery they fought their illness. It is also dedicated to their loved ones, who suffered, struggled, and fought alongside them.

About the Authors

Paul J. Antonellis, Jr., MA, CEAP, CAS is a former fire chief with over 19 years of fire service experience and 11 years of law enforcement experience. His education includes a Master's Degree in Labor and Policy Studies with a concentration in Human Resource Management, a Bachelor of Science Degree in Fire Service Administration, and Associate Degrees in Criminal Justice and Fire Service Technology. He is a Certified Employee Assistance Professional (CEAP), Certified Addictions Specialist (CAS), and a licensed Massachusetts Alcohol and Drug Counselor. Mr. Antonellis currently serves as a part-time faculty member in the Fire Service Program at Empire State College and is an instructor for the Massachusetts Fire Academy. In addition, Mr. Antonellis teaches nationally and internationally for the International Critical Incident Stress Foundation where he co-developed their Line-of-Duty Death program. He has published several articles and one other book entitled *A Guide to Help the Fire Service Prepare for a Line of Duty Death or Injury.*

Shannon Gwin Mitchell, PhD is a researcher at Johns Hopkins University where she currently conducts community-based AIDS prevention research with injection drug users. Dr. Mitchell is on the editorial board of the *International Journal of Emergency Mental Health* and serves as a reviewer for several international journals specializing in issues of mental health as well as qualitative research and methodology. She received her doctorate in Community and Social Psychology from the

University of Maryland, Baltimore County, her Master's Degree in Clinical Psychology from the University of South Dakota, and her Bachelor's Degree in Psychology from the University of California, Riverside, where she studied and researched Personality Psychology. Dr. Mitchell has been involved in the traumatic stress field since 1993. She has been trained in Critical Incident Stress Management and EMDR and worked as a psychometrician prior to entering the research field. She and her husband live in Woodbine, Maryland, with their two young daughters.

Acknowledgements

I would personally like to thank Dr. John Greene for his advice, his constant pushing, and support during this process. Without his help this endeavor would not have been possible. I can honestly say I will never look at a psychologist the same after meeting and working with you, Dr. Greene. You are truly a credit to the fire service. In addition, I would like to thank Michael Sacco, Doctor Ofra Sarid-Segal, David Akin, Neal Braverman, our publisher, our editor, and all the wonderful people who helped provide the quotes within the book. A special thanks to those who shared their stories with me. I can honestly say that without each and every one of you this book would not have turned out the way it did.

Paul J. Antonellis, Jr., MA, CEAP, CAS

Fall 2004

I would like to thank our publisher for giving us this wonderful opportunity and my family for permitting me long hours and late nights in front of the computer.

Shannon Gwin Mitchell, PhD

Fall 2004

viii

Contents

About the Title

Most firefighters perform a job every day that the average person cannot fully comprehend, much less duplicate. They risk their lives to help others, they witness people at their most vulnerable, and they do it all with professionalism and compassion.

If you are a firefighter, you know that most of the time the understanding that "it's just a job" is enough to keep you from being personally impacted by what you do or see. However, sometimes there are those calls that are not so easily left behind at the scene. The calls that "stick with you" long after the turnout gear has been hung up and the shift has ended. The calls that haunt you in your dreams, that remind you of your own mortality, that make you question your competency (even when undeserved) and avoid the things that you always loved most about your work.

This book is about those calls that stick with you.

Preface

This book seeks to fill a void in the literature on Post-traumatic Stress Disorder (PTSD) by examining the phenomenon not just from the vantage point of fire personnel but by doing so through the stories of firefighters themselves. In this book we present the case stories of three firefighters who, in the course of doing their jobs, developed PTSD. These men were affected by different types of stressors at different points in their careers, but the tremendous impact that the psychological trauma had on their lives is undeniable.

While firefighters are at increased risk for developing PTSD as compared to the general population, there remains a cloud of uncertainty surrounding the disorder in the fire service: uncertainty concerning which reactions are normal, whether or not they should be spoken of with colleagues and family members, and when and where to seek help. We wrote this book for firefighters and their families so that they would have a better understanding of PTSD: how it looks, why it develops, where to get help (if you already have it), and how to prevent it (if you are lucky enough to be in a pro-active department).

The book begins with an overview of why firefighters deserve special consideration when it comes to PTSD: what makes them tick, what kinds of things they are expected to do on the job, and how personality and environmental factors contribute to their increased likelihood of developing PTSD. You may recognize yourself or your loved one in the first two chapters. The intent of these chapters is to draw attention to the aspects of personality and environment that work well most of the time, and are even beneficial much of the time, but that can sometimes set a firefighter up for trouble.

We will then present a brief overview of exactly what Posttraumatic Stress Disorder (PTSD) and Acute Stress Disorder (ASD) are, including general diagnostic criteria and some brief information on related disorders. This chapter may help you in identifying just how traumatized you, or someone you know, may be. If the symptoms look too familiar for comfort, rest assured that you are not alone.

Chapters 4 through 6 are the case stories of three different firefighters who developed PTSD while doing their job. The names of the people in all three stories have been changed, but the details in the stories have not. Experiences ranged from personal injury in a chemical explosion to vicarious traumatization by assisting rescue workers following a large-scale disaster. These three cases were selected because the people involved were kind and brave enough to share their stories and because they represent a wide range of experiences, showing that traumatization does not have to occur just when your own life has been threatened or just when you are a young, green probie, fresh out of the academy.

The latter part of the book is all about help: where to find it when you or someone whom you know has been psychologically injured and how to help healthy personnel stay healthy. The part of the book that is often overlooked by readers, the appendices and reference sections, will provide you with additional sources of information on PTSD, treatment, research, etc. We encourage you to explore these sections, check out some of the websites, look up some of the references, pass them on to others who may need them, and help yourself or someone else begin the healing process if psychological trauma has already occurred.

This book is not meant to be used as a diagnostic tool, but it may help you recognize when you or someone whom you know may need more help. It can be a very slippery slope from "bothersome" to "intrusive" or from "disturbing" to "debilitating." All the firefighters in the cases we present had some aspect of an incident "stick with them" in a way that made it impossible to put it behind them. Their "bad call" began to consume their lives.

While this book was written with firefighters and their families in mind, we believe it can be useful to others as well. Clinicians who want to work with firefighters can gain a better understanding of common firefighter personality traits and job characteristics by reading this book. In addition, much can be learned by fire administrators who want to see how their own responses to a traumatized firefighter may impact the course of healing.

The three men who shared their personal stories for this book did so with the hope that it would serve to increase awareness of PTSD in the fire service and help other firefighters stay healthy and have long, productive, satisfying careers. We sincerely echo this hope.

Chapter One

What Makes a Firefighter?

*"Among the personal qualities firefighters need are
mental alertness, self-discipline, courage, mechanical
aptitude, endurance, strength, and a sense of public
service. Initiative and good judgment are also
extremely important because firefighters make quick
decisions in emergencies. Because members of a
crew live and work closely together under conditions
of stress and danger for extended periods, they must
be dependable and able to get along well with others.
Leadership qualities are necessary for officers, who
must establish and maintain discipline and
efficiency, as well as direct the activities
of firefighters in their companies."*
(Firefighting Occupations, OSHA website, 2004)

Hardly a day goes by without hearing a story of a firefighter taking a risk to save another person's life. Ahrens of the National Fire Protection Association (NFPA; 2004) has reported that the United States has one of the worst fire death rates per capita in the industrialized world. During 2002 there was a civilian fire death every 28 minutes, in addition to thousands of civilian injuries.

Not only are firefighters confronted with traumatic incidents on a regular basis, they must also deal with the fact that often their own personal safety is placed at risk when they respond to an incident. On average, 100 firefighters are killed in the line of duty each year across the United States and more than 80,000 work-related injuries occur, often requiring hospitalization (Lee, Fleming, Gomez-Marin, & LeBlanc, 2004; U.S. Fire Administration

[USFA], 2004). Given these staggering statistics, one can see that being a firefighter in the United States is a very dangerous occupation. It goes without saying that firefighters constantly walk a professional tightrope, balancing risk and reward.

So then, what would make someone want to take on a career where they are sure to be confronted with trauma and stress? In other words, "What makes a firefighter?" To answer this question one must look at some of the characteristics of people commonly drawn to the fire profession, including

- Being detail oriented
- Possessing a strong motivation to succeed
- Thrill-seeking

The Firefighter Personality

While you can just as easily argue that the fire service culture impacts how a firefighter behaves, many firefighters (and their family members) would say that they were made for their chosen career, some at a very early age. Anecdotal evidence would tend to suggest a self-selection process in that people who possess the personality traits that make them suitable for a career in the fire service may gravitate in that direction, while people with personalities unsuitable for life as a firefighter tend to avoid those types of jobs. A recent empirical examination of the personalities of firefighters (Peters & Scott, 2003) supports the idea that firefighters possess some personality traits that are quite different from the general population. This is what many refer to as "the firefighter personality."

Details, Details, Details

One of the first things that you will notice about the average firefighter is an incredible attention to detail (Holborn, 2002; Mitchell & Bray, 1990). Some call it "meticulous," others "obsessive-compulsive." In the end, it is this wonderful attention to detail that allows a firefighter to go into very chaotic and dangerous situations and feel a sense of control. You never know exactly how a fire is going to react, but it helps to know that you can count on your equipment and the guys on your crew. The average firefighter will take the Boy Scout motto, "Be prepared," to new heights.

Emergencies, by definition, are unexpected events, so firefighters spend much of their time trying to be prepared for (if not expecting) the unexpected, and the fire culture encourages and enhances their perfectionist tendencies. Take one look at any fire apparatus and you will find a very clean, well-organized, and properly maintained piece of equipment. (Civilians unfamiliar with the fire service sometimes think that firefighters have nothing better to do with their time than clean their trucks.) The real reason for this, of course, is that a well-maintained apparatus is also a dependable apparatus.

3

Another part of being prepared for the unexpected is to do things over and over until they are perfectly executed and become rote. Ask any firefighter how many times they have practiced ladder drills, tying knots in rope, or putting on and taking off the air pack. The answer will most likely be, "So many times I could do it in my sleep." Repetitive training is conducted to increase the firefighter's proficiency in the skill so that they can respond the same way during an emergency call without wasting precious time. It also increases comfort and familiarity with these skills, thereby enhancing the feeling of control (Bellrose & Pilisuk, 1991).

Perfectionism also motivates a firefighter to "tinker" with better ways of doing a job. For example, a firefighter may have pried open a door at an accident scene or in training numerous times, yet still take time on their day off to go down to a salvage yard and practice prying apart wrecked vehicles, in search of developing the "perfect" way of doing it or of shaving off a few more seconds of time.

Success Is Not Optional

Another common aspect of many firefighter personalities is a deep desire to be successful. Always. And part of being successful is "mission completion." If the job is not finished then you obviously were not successful.

One common rule of thumb is: Tell a firefighter what you want done and how you want it done, give them the tools and training to do it, and then get the hell out of their way! Firefighters will sometimes work tirelessly to complete a task or assignment successfully, even if it means putting themselves at risk to do so.

Looking for Thrills

Most firefighters are easily bored and may spend their free time engaging in highly stimulating sports and other exciting activities (Mitchell & Bray, 1990). Part of the thrill-seeking behavior of firefighters is related to their need for control and success. This probably sounds paradoxical at first. Control and thrill-seeking seem to be at opposite ends of the spectrum, but think about it. By engaging in thrill-seeking behaviors, a person is constantly testing the limits of their control and setting the bar for success at higher and higher levels. Anyone can maintain control of a vehicle doing 50 mph but how many people can successfully control a vehicle doing 90 mph... in the rain... on a windy road? (And if the other guy could do it at 90, I'll bet I could control it while doing 95.)

Some people may actually be drawn to firefighting because it is considered a high-risk occupation. Unlike occupations in the service sector, where people are often unaware of the risks associated with their choice of career, those who choose to become firefighters know that risk is part of the job (Bellrose & Pilisuk, 1991), and many of them wouldn't have it any other way.

It's Not What You Do, It's Who You Are

Fire personnel do not just "fight fires," they ARE firefighters. It is more than an occupation. It is an identity. They will have a license plate signifying that they are a firefighter or possibly some sort of sticker on their vehicle indicating that they belong to the fire service. They will wear fire department insignia clothing such as tee-shirts or ball caps in their off-duty time. Firefighters are very proud of their occupation, and anyone speaking ill of the fire service is in for a battle; these waters run deep and swift.

Because a firefighter's job is so closely linked with their identity, losing one's job due to disability or retirement can be personally devastating. The longer a firefighter is away from the fire service because of an injury, the harder it is to return. As time passes, they become separated from the fire service and have less and less in common. Meeting up with fellow firefighters, the injured firefighter begins to feel "out of the loop" and lacking the commonality that once held them so close.

Links of a Chain

Firefighters work and live in a group environment. From the very first time recruits walk into a fire station, they learn that firefighting is a team sport. Firefighters train in groups, work in groups, live in groups, and even eat in groups. As a profession, firefighters are very unique in the degree to which they share a bond with one another. And it is the perceived support that firefighters get from one another that contributes to high levels of job satisfaction among fire personnel, despite relatively low pay (Bellrose & Pilisuk, 1991).

So what do you get when you put a dozen or more detail-oriented, success-driven people on one team? One hell of a good team!

Accepting Responsibility:
The Good, the Bad and the Ugly

All the typical characteristics mentioned above—being meticulous, control-oriented, motivated to succeed, and thrill-seeking—help the firefighter do a job that most people could not do. However, these same characteristics can sometimes come back to haunt a firefighter when a mission turns out ugly.

Remember that extreme need to plan out details in order to promote a sense of control? It can lead to assuming personal responsibility for aspects of an incident that were actually out of the firefighter's control (Mitchell & Bray, 1990). The "I could have, would have, should have, if only I had..." thoughts (even when obviously related to things that could not, would not, and should not have gone differently) can eat a firefighter up after a "failed" mission.

Do you remember that thrill-seeking tendency to push the envelope? It can lead to doing very risky things during an operation that put the firefighter, and sometimes others, into greater situations of risk than are actually necessary. According to Holt (1988), "It isn't until you do start to look at why firefighters do what they do that you can begin to define 'heroic' behavior as a strength or a liability" (p. 32). One of the greatest accomplishments a firefighter can have is "making a save." Making a save is when a firefighter saves a human life, and nothing in the world can be as rewarding to a firefighter. After all, that is what it's all about.

And remember the "team work" aspect of the job? No one wants to be the weak link in the chain and let the others down in an emergency. And, of course, no one wants to be considered a coward or a failure in the eyes of their crewmates. This can also lead one to take more risks during an operation than would normally be expected.

In Summary

To be a firefighter takes a very special person: a sociable person who is willing to put the needs of others before their own, who enjoys the thrills of the job but can still handle the technical details, and who possesses a strong desire to complete a task successfully. Not all firefighters will possess all of these traits, but most firefighters will possess many of them. These traits may draw them to a career as a firefighter where those same traits are then reinforced by the academy and the larger fire culture. However, it is important to remember that the things that make a firefighter effective on the job when things go as planned can also be the things that devastate that same firefighter when things go wrong.

don't think this last comment applies just to volunteers), firefighters often find themselves in this physical and mental "ready state," which affects the way they handle other aspects of their lives and the people with whom they interact.

Often call or volunteer firefighters will say they are "never" off duty. For a variety of reasons, they may even have several scanner radios on in their house and leave them on 24/7. This, of course, only serves to reinforce the constant feeling of needing to be ready and reduces the firefighters' ability to relax when away from work. Even when it is not their shift, most firefighters are looking for clues that will tell them when "The Big One" is about to hit and they will be called in to help. Add to this the stresses of shift work and an ever-changing work schedule, and one can easily see how a firefighter's job can consume other aspects of their life.

So when they're on, they're on—and when they're off, they're on. What happens to a car when you let it idle at high speeds for prolonged periods of time? Excessive wear and tear beyond that which would be expected based on the mileage. And what happens when you let a body "idle" at high speeds for prolonged periods of time? Excessive wear and tear on the body beyond what would be expected for one's age. The tendency to always be in a ready state does more than simply annoy your spouse. It can also have a negative impact on your long-term health. Couple that with the toxins and environmental hazards that are part and parcel of the job (as well as the unhealthy lifestyle practices that we see in many firefighters) and you have the recipe for some serious health problems.

Who Said Anything about Sleep?

In a majority of firehouses across the country, firefighters working the night shift are allowed to sleep at night or "rest between runs." But because they are maintaining that physical and mental ready state around the clock, any sleep that is obtained can hardly be considered a sound night of sleep. The result is that even a night shift without any calls can lead to sleep deprivation and fatigue. To add insult to injury, some people who do not understand the job will make comments such as, "All you did was sleep last night. How can you possibly be tired?"

This type of "sleepless sleep" is actually a form of sleep deprivation. Researchers have compared the effects of sleep deprivation to alcohol impairment beyond a .05 blood alcohol level (Williamson & Feyer, 2000). In addition to problems with coordination, reaction time, and judgment (all of which can negatively affect job performance), other known effects of sleep deprivation include weakening of the immune system (making a person more susceptible to everything from colds to cancer) and changes in mental processes (causing confusion, memory problems, and irritability) (Cardinal, 2004). Add a weakened immune system to the regular exposure to sick individuals that a firefighter encounters on a tour of duty (flu, common colds, and communicable diseases) and you have the makings of an employee who may be performing at less than optimal levels. In general, sleep deprivation causes stress. And more stress is definitely not something that most firefighters need.

Ready, Set, Wait

Firefighters always want to be ready for "The Big One" when it hits. Fortunately (or unfortunately, depending on how you look it at), "The Big One" does not hit on every shift of every day. Depending on your station, you may not even get "The Little One" very often. Stations in sparsely populated areas or communities in which prevention efforts have been successful may go the entire shift without even so much as a false alarm. So what is an "always be prepared" firefighter going to do with all that time and all that energy? Most of it is spent on preparation- and prevention-related activities: conducting trainings and drills, preparing and servicing equipment and apparatus, etc.

To fill remaining down time, firefighters are hardly at a loss for things to do. Chief among those activities are the mundane housekeeping chores for the firehouse: rugs need to be vacuumed, floors need to be washed, meals need to be cooked, and bathrooms need to be cleaned. (It has been rumored that some firefighters will actually work harder at getting out of these daily chores than if they had just done the job in the first place.)

13

More importantly, firefighters are also responsible for maintaining their equipment. Time at the station is spent ensuring that the vehicles they drive are properly serviced and in good working order and that their equipment and gear is clean, functional, and ready for use. Firefighters commonly utilize a systematic approach to checking their vehicles and equipment: engine oil, vehicle fuel, warning lights, horns, brakes, water, side mirrors, pump operation/ladder operation, tire pressure, loose equipment, headlights, and turn signals. However, while these tasks may be both critical and time consuming, most fire personnel do not consider them an enjoyable part of the job and may feel that a shift spent on maintenance issues is, essentially, a wasted shift.

Bureaucracy and Politics

For some firefighters, the most stressful aspect of the job is the bureaucracy and management to be dealt with on a regular basis. Most firefighters are civil servants (with the exception of those employed in a private industry) and must rely on elected officials for their departmental budgets, their continued employment, and even many of the regulations under which they must work. However, most bureaucrats are unfamiliar with the fire service and, truth be told, nothing in government ever seems to get done quickly (a marked contrast to life in the firehouse.)

Many fire departments across the U.S. are currently dealing with budget cutbacks and find that the crews at their stations must work short shifted. A common complaint from firefighters across the county is the lack of support and proper funding from municipal, state, and federal government officials. As a result, fire departments may be dealing with old equipment and failing facilities at a time when they are being asked to be prepared for everything from bio-terrorism to natural disasters.

Bureaucratic stressors are a hassle not just for the firefighters. Fire service administrators are also frequently faced with a certain level of bureaucratic strain. They must address the work-related concerns and complaints of the firefighters on one side and the accountability and funding concerns of community leaders on the other.

Administrators may feel that they are caught in the

middle, accountable to both sides yet not really trusted or accepted by either. This position places fire service administrators in a class of their own. For this reason it is very common to find a very tight bond among fire chiefs, especially since their numbers are so few when compared to the number of firefighters they manage. Once a person is admitted into a fire chief position, they are almost automatically accepted into the very special social support group they create. Support may come from other fire chiefs in the next community or from several states away.

Never the Same Day Twice

For some people, a very fluid work environment is less than desirable. They may need more predictability in what they do, or when they eat, or even how much sleep they get. Usually these people will avoid careers in the fire service, but once in a while a bright, dedicated cadet who may be unsuitable for the chaos of the job will sneak through the fire academy. And when they do, they may find that they have spent several months training for a job that they dislike, and the department may find that they have spent thousands of dollars training the wrong person for a job that, once again, needs to be filled.

15

A case in point is the story of one firefighter who had worked in banking for several years prior to taking his firefighter entrance exam. The banker was hired and attended the recruit school with flying colors, graduating with top honors in his class. (Keep in mind that the training school is a controlled environment: when class starts, what topics will be covered, when there will be a break for lunch, and when the day ends are all scheduled and predictable.)

The following week the new firefighter reported to work at his assigned fire station where he quickly discovered that the fire station was not like anything he had ever experienced before. A call was received within the first minute of his shift, with no time to prepare his new gear and no time for a shift briefing. He was simply told to grab his gear and get on the truck. The firefighter quickly realized that lunch was almost never at noon and that drills were seldom fully completed by all of the shift members. In the end, the firefighter resigned after only 10 weeks on the job. His reason cited for leaving was the fact that he could not work in such a disruptive environment. Some people hate it, some people love it, but it comes with the territory. That is why it is so critical that people who join the fire service are more than just physically and mentally prepared for the work that they are required to do. They must also be able to deal with their work environment: in the department, at the station, and on scene.

16

On Scene

Go!

One moment you are diligently completing a report and the next moment your senses are being flooded with blaring sirens and bodies in motion. A firefighter's environment can change with the ring of a 911 phone line and go from controlled to chaotic almost instantaneously.

Many fire station building designs pay considerable attention to the notification process of emergency calls for firefighters. Historically, fire stations have had large horns blow, bells ring, and/or all of the fire station lights turn on high in an effort to notify the on-duty firefighters of a call. This was necessary in the days before portable radios, cell phones, and more reliable radio systems. However, old habits seem to die hard in the fire service, and today many stations still use jarring notification systems. This is done despite the growing knowledge that this form of notification can be another source of strain for the firefighter, producing an exacerbation of the startle response (International Fire Service Training Association [IFSTA], 1992). Some fire personnel have even reported having an off duty startle response to sights and sounds that are similar to the notification process(es) of their station. For example, a firefighter taking a nap on the sofa at home can produce an exaggerated startle response if someone walks into the room and flips on the lights.

New fire station designs are now seriously considering the notification process they use, and the loud, intrusive horns, bells, and lights are being toned down or, in some cases, replaced altogether in favor of less jarring techniques. The sleeping quarters in newer fire stations are beginning to use soft blue lights in an effort to prevent blinding bright lights as a firefighter awakens from sleep.

17

Sorry, False Alarm

Any firefighter will tell you that dealing with false alarms can be a frustrating part of the job. However in the fire service, every call is handled as an emergency response until proven otherwise. During the typical fire department response, the fire apparatus will utilize emergency warning lights and audible noise. The firefighter becomes accustomed to flashing lights, sirens, and air horn noises during emergency responses. (These same warning devices can later become an audible cue for firefighters suffering from PTSD.) Unfortunately the body is unable to distinguish a real call from a false alarm and will take some time to return to a level of homeostasis. In the meantime, the firefighter is on an adrenaline-fueled roller coaster ride as adrenaline is pumped into the blood stream to provide energy for the firefighter's response. However, if the call is a false alarm, this adrenaline is being pumped throughout the body but not being used for anything constructive. This may occur several times per day so that by the end of the day the firefighter will have experienced unusually high levels of adrenaline. If the firefighter is fortunate enough to be able to hit the gym for a full workout at the end of shift, that adrenaline can be constructively "worked off."

False calls can also be a source of frustration to the firefighter unable to finish a report or a task. To be interrupted for a legitimate reason is one thing, but to be interrupted for a false alarm can be down-right maddening, especially for a task-oriented person. This feeling of frustration can be carried into the next call for service or taken out on other crewmembers. In addition, interruptions may not only interfere with the ability to complete the task or report but may also increase the chance for errors.

Being sent to "staging" can be just as frustrating as a false call. Staging is employed for the safe and effective utilization of responding resources during an incident. In some cases apparatus and personnel sent to staging are never used at an incident but are held in reserve, if needed. To the average firefighter this can be a very frustrating waste of time. Remember, firefighters are action-orientated people, and staging is definitely not where the action is.

You're Very Welcome

While most people are extremely grateful for the assistance they receive, occasionally a firefighter will find that the person they are trying to help is less than appreciative, and sometimes even downright abusive. Some people may become caustic because their house is filling up with thousands of gallons of water (forget the fact that the water is being put there to extinguish a fire). They can be hypercritical of the tactics or care being used to help them, even when they are not in a position to understand. Others can sometimes be verbally or physically abusive when they see their home being destroyed or a loved one in pain while the firefighters are not in an immediate position to help. "You saved my home but no one is helping me find my dog!" "Just wait 'til I tell my insurance adjuster what you did to my front door!" "What took you so long to get here?" If unfortunate situations such as this arise, maintaining a professional demeanor in the face of such ingratitude can be difficult to do, and dealing with abusive "customers" can suck the joy out of the job for some fire personnel.

High Risk Responses

While the majority of the incidents that firefighters respond to are standard fare, some are memorable, and others are down right unforgettable. Within this last category lie certain types of incidents that, often for unpleasant reasons, seem to stick with the firefighter long after the incident has wrapped up and the shift has ended. Sometimes such incidents are memorable because of who was involved. Other times they have an impact because of what happened to the firefighter personally, to other members of the crew, or to the civilians involved. These types of incidents are important because they can compound the other, more normal stressors present in the firefighter's job and have a negative cumulative effect when they build up over many years of service.

That Person Looks a Lot Like . . .

It can be very difficult for a firefighter to deal with a victim who resembles a familiar person: son or daughter, mother or father, spouse, or even the firefighter him- or herself. Part of what enables an emergency responder to function effectively in a crisis situation is the ability to maintain emotional distance and remain objective. Seeing a victim but thinking of someone whom you love pops the objectivity bubble and the firefighter may begin to make emotional rather than rational decisions. Sometimes the objectivity is compromised on scene, such as when the firefighter arrives and is immediately reminded of a loved one. Other times the case becomes more personal afterwards when firefighters realize they are comparing the victim to themselves or a loved one. This may cloud the actual memory of what happened on scene and make the firefighter more critical of their job performance on the incident.

Another difficult type of response that is more common in, but not the sole domain of, rural areas occurs when the firefighter actually knows the victim. If having the victim simply resemble someone whom you know can be difficult, imagine how hard it can be when they really are someone whom you know. We all strive to provide the best possible care for everyone, but there can be another whole level of urgency when we know the victim. It can also be acutely painful to find yourself helpless to assist someone whom you know and love when they need you the most.

The Most Vulnerable Victims

Children are supposed to be protected, they are supposed to have long, healthy lives and, because they are innocent and good, bad things should not happen to them. Unfortunately, the rules are sometimes broken and children get seriously hurt, sometimes by the very people who are supposed to be taking care of them. Seeing a child who has been seriously injured or killed can be one of the most difficult scenes a firefighter has to face. And the feelings of helplessness or anger may be even more intense if firefighters have their own children at home to think about.

21

You Never Thought It Could Happen to You

Although every firefighter knows that there are significant risks that come with the job, no one ever thinks that they might be the one who gets injured. As we mentioned in Chapter 1, every year thousands of firefighters are injured on the job, some minor, some serious—and over one hundred lose their lives. Firefighters who are injured in the line of duty are likely to face numerous physical and psychological challenges. Some will recuperate and return to work. Others may find themselves unable to perform their job following the injury and lose not only their livelihood but their identity as well.

Being injured in the line of duty may make a firefighter feel scrutinized (if others question whether or not the firefighter's own actions directly contributed to the injury), isolated, and responsible (especially if another firefighter was also injured in the incident). All of these reactions are painful for a team-oriented, sociable person.

In some ways, the state-of-the-art firefighting equipment used today may actually contribute to increased risk exposure and increased injury on the job. In one research study (Woods, 2001), a positive link was identified between the amount of fully encapsulated fire gear worn and the level of risk firefighters were willing to take. Sensory deprivation appears to be one of the mechanisms linking the two together. In some cases, wearing fully encapsulated gear may give the firefighter a false sense of security and actually contribute to increased risk taking.

The "F" Word

22

Any time a firefighter does everything right but the end result is a loss of life or property, the firefighter may consider it a "Failure." (And task-oriented, competitive people do not like to fail.) Often there was nothing that the firefighter did wrong. Maybe even more was done than was expected, given the situation. But hindsight can be cruel, expectations can be unreasonable, and control-oriented people sometimes take responsibility for things which are beyond their control.

Preparing and Protecting Your Own

Proactive fire departments have been attempting to prepare their personnel for this ever-changing environment. Some have implemented a screening process to ensure that the candidates have a very clear understanding of what the job of firefighter entails and to ensure that the department has safe and healthy firefighters. Some fire administrators are admitting that critical incident stress has an effect on their employees and are offering the needed support through EAPs and critical incident stress management (CISM) teams. Recognizing that human capital is an enormous expense, fire department administrators, are taking steps to ensure that their "capital" is in good, working condition.

Unfortunately this is not yet a universal standard. A fire service may screen firefighter candidates for mental health issues when they are hired, but most do little to ensure the continued mental health of their employees. Many smaller departments cannot afford even to conduct pre-employment screenings, never mind post-employment screenings. Perhaps the International Association of Firefighters and the International Association of Fire Chiefs could create a joint partnership for developing a standard mental health screening process for firefighters. From the day candidates are accepted into the fire service until the day they retire, the department should do everything in its power to ensure that firefighters remain physically and psychologically healthy.

23

What It Can Do to You

Going into the fire service, firefighters know that they will be exposed to death and dying. Regardless, it does not make the process any easier. During a fire response to a residential house fire, the dispatcher reports that a child may be trapped inside the house. On arrival, the firefighters are confronted with several adults attempting to enter the burning building in an effort to save the child. The fire chief assigns a search and rescue crew to search the area where the child was last seen and a medical crew to evaluate the burns on the adults.

The medical crew must not only deal with the physical injuries (the burns); they must also deal with the psychological injuries of the child's parents. The firefighter must comfort them and treat their injuries knowing that they may possibly have just witnessed their child burning to death in their own home.

For the crews assigned to search for the child, seconds feel like hours. They try in vain to locate the child, pushing their equipment and their bodies to the limits. To the firefighters, the only noise heard is the pounding of their heart; the scene seems so silent, the operation seems to slow to a snail's pace, and everything is clouded in smoke and uncertainty.

24

In reality, the scene is very noisy, filled with commotion and what would appear to the untrained eye like total confusion. Yet this is the operation of a well-oiled machine. One of the firefighter/paramedics finds the body of the little boy on the bedroom floor behind the door. The firefighter exits the building with the burned body lying limp in their arms. The little body seems weightless to the firefighter as they return to the front yard of the house, met by additional paramedics and ambulance personnel. The ambulance crew begins treating the boy and transports him to the hospital where he soon dies from his injuries.

The news of the child's death travels quickly back to the fire scene. Many of the firefighters view this as a "failed" mission. Why? Because a person died. The firefighters begin to feel that they could have done things better or differently. What they fail to see is how they prevented additional deaths from occurring. Their actions prevented the child's parents from re-entering the house and possibly dying in the fire as well. What would have happened if no one had helped the parents at the scene?

Firefighters often look at the negative side and forget to look at the overall good that they provided. The house fire was extinguished and no further damage was done to any adjacent property. Most importantly, no one else died. However, in spite of everything the firefighters did right, they may still find that the feeling of having that light, limp body in their arms or the image of the anguish on the parents' faces is with them every time they close their eyes to sleep.

The Invisible Crew Member

A final area that must be discussed is the firefighter's family. Some fire departments make a point of informing the family of what the job consists of and how it may affect both the individual firefighter and the larger family unit. When the first author of this book was serving as Fire Chief, he told new firefighters, "When you signed on the dotted line to join the fire department you did not just sign yourself up, you signed up your entire family."

A fire department should be concerned with the firefighter's family and the effect the job is having on them. Ask any fire chief and you will be informed that if a firefighter's home life is not in balance, it will tend to show up at work. And if this is the case, firefighters may inadvertently place themselves or their fellow firefighters at risk. It is very important that firefighters be 100% physically and psychologically fit for duty, or they may be doing a disservice to themselves, their co-workers, and their families.

In Summary

This chapter addressed some of the common environmental aspects of being a firefighter, at the station and on scene. Sources of stress included the need to maintain a "ready state" of preparedness, sleep deprivation, long periods of boredom between call-outs, the demands of dealing with administrative and bureaucratic issues, and the sudden changes in the environment. On scene a firefighter is likely to experience numerous false alarms, difficult clientele, and situations that can be psychologically upsetting for a variety of reasons. Other factors that can cause additional stress for the firefighter include working with a patient whom the firefighter knows (or who looks like a familiar person), dealing with an injured or deceased child, experiencing a line-of-duty injury, and interpreting a call that ends in a loss of life as a "failure." Increasingly, fire departments are recognizing that these types of stressors not only negatively affect the firefighters but can affect their families as well.

Chapter Three

Traumatic Stress Reactions: PTSD, ASD, and Related Disorders

While the odds indicate that many firefighters will be exposed to a traumatic incident at some point in their careers, many of them will be able to resolve the trauma without formal clinical assistance. They may find that their symptoms subside after they talk about the incident with co-workers or simply as time passes. For others, however, the early symptoms will stay with them or even worsen. Some may develop other problems, such as acute changes in their personality or a dependency on drugs or alcohol in an attempt to manage their symptoms. Family, friends, and co-workers may know that the firefighter is having trouble but not realize just how severe it is, especially if the firefighter is isolating from others. And even if they have some idea of the problems that the firefighter is experiencing, they might not be able to distinguish a normal reaction from a clinical one or know when to recommend that the person seek treatment.

As is the case with many psychological disorders, traumatic stress symptoms tend to lie along a continuum. The difference between normal and pathological can sometimes be a matter of degrees (in symptom intensity or duration) and the severity of the impact on the person's life can be affected by their level of functioning prior to the incident as well as the coping skills that are employed after the exposure. With that said, it is important to remember that anyone might develop PTSD if the incident is severe enough—regardless of age, experience, or rank.

The first two chapters of this book addressed personality and environmental factors commonly found among firefighters: factors such as bravery, altruism, and a work environment filled with unknown hazards and potential risks to self and others. By almost any standard, firefighting would be considered a stressful profession. But when does the stress become "traumatic stress?" To help the reader understand and recognize traumatic stress and its sequelae we will begin with a description of how traumatic stress first became recognized as a psychological disorder and how our conceptualization of the disorder has developed as a result of our study and understanding of different groups of traumatized persons (e.g., war veterans, victims of rape, people affected by natural or manmade disasters). We will then present a brief description of the two DSM-IV diagnoses directly associated with exposure to a traumatic event: Acute Stress Disorder (ASD) and Posttraumatic Stress Disorder (PTSD).

28

One of the factors that can sometimes make it difficult to identify PTSD or ASD is that other disorders may also be present, masking the primary traumatic stress symptoms. The most common secondary disorders that are found in someone who has been traumatized include depression and drug or alcohol abuse/dependency. For this reason we will also present a brief description of those disorders. Our final step in linking traumatic stress with fire personnel will be to discuss what we know about the incidence and prevalence of psychological trauma in firefighters. This will provide you with an appreciation of just how common it is to find firefighter stories similar to the ones presented in chapters 4 through 6.

The purpose of the present chapter is not to enable the reader to "diagnose" PTSD in themselves or another person. Primarily it is intended to help the reader better understand and appreciate the case stories presented in this book. However, the secondary purpose of this chapter (and the book as a whole) is to increase knowledge and awareness of traumatic stress and the significant toll it can take on firefighters, their careers, and their families and to help the reader recognize when someone is in need of professional assistance. For additional information on diagnoses and for psychological referral information, please see the appendices at the back of the book (Appendix A: DSM-IV criteria for PTSD; Appendix B: DSM-IV criteria for ASD; Appendix C: Resource and referral information).

What Is Trauma?

Trauma and its effects on psychological functioning were first recognized among soldiers on the battlefields of war. Terms such as "shell shock," "battle fatigue," and "combat neuroses" were used as far back as the American Civil War to describe the psychological numbing and intense startle reactions that many soldiers experienced as a result of their exposure to death and dismemberment (Mitchell & Everly, 1993). When veterans returned home from World War II, it became apparent that they were dealing with much more than physical wounds, and when the first Diagnostic and Statistical Manual of Mental Disorders (DSM) was created in 1952, it was the experiences of those veterans and the survivors of the concentration camps that helped mold the original traumatic stress diagnosis, called Gross Stress Reaction.

In the last 50 years, the DSM has been revised several times and so has the diagnosis associated with exposure to trauma. Vietnam veterans contributed significantly to our understanding of traumatic stress, as have victims of sexual assault, victims of natural disasters (such as earthquakes or tornadoes), and victims of man-made disasters (such as plane crashes) (Friedman, 2003; Schiraldi, 2000). No doubt our knowledge of terrorism and the trauma it produces will be expanded even more in the coming years as longitudinal studies involving survivors of September 11 are published in the research literature.

The criteria for exactly what constitutes a "traumatic experience" has also evolved over the years. In the DSM-III-R version of PTSD, trauma was defined as an experience "outside the range of normal human experience" that most people would consider upsetting (American Psychiatric Association [APA], 1987). When the DSM went into its 4th edition the criteria became more specific, entailing the threat of death or serious injury. (APA, 2000). The DSM-IV also included the new diagnosis of Acute Stress Disorder (ASD), which accounted for the more immediate stress reaction. Until that time a diagnosis concerning psychological trauma could only be given one month or later after symptoms first appeared, making it more difficult for a provider to address a recent trauma in therapy (insurance companies often refuse to pay for care if a diagnosis is not provided).

From the earliest conceptualizations of traumatic stress reactions, fear and anxiety emerged as the central components—not surprising considering that the two are intricately linked with one another. In fact, the exact same physical sensations (racing heart, sweating, shallow breathing, etc.) may be labeled as "fear" when in a dangerous or threatening situation but labeled as "anxiety" when there are no external cues indicating that a person's safety is in jeopardy (Horowitz, 1997). When a person has intrusive memories of a traumatic experience, their body will go through many of the same sensations that were experienced during the trauma. At the time of the incident, the physical sensations were probably correctly identified as being the result of fear. When those same physical sensations are re-experienced during an intrusive memory of the event, but the physical safety of the person is no longer an issue, they would be considered anxiety reactions.

It is important to point out that feelings of fear or anxiety, anger or sadness are quite common after experiencing a traumatic event and are not a stand-alone sign that a person will develop ASD or PTSD. They are normal reactions to an abnormal event. A firefighter who responds to a fatal car accident in which the victim strongly resembles someone whom they love may feel some anxiety when they first see the victim or after the operation is complete. Those types of incidents increase our awareness concerning the fragility of life, something that most of us hardly ever think about as we go through our daily lives. Having mild anxiety when thing about the incident is normal. Thinking about it frequently in the days following the incident is normal. Not wanting to talk about the incident is also understandable if it was extremely upsetting (although talking about it and discussing why it was so upsetting to you may actually help you work through the feelings more rapidly). It is when these thoughts and feelings begin to interfere with a person's life, personally or professionally, or when they become distressing and do not subside over time, that professional assistance should be sought out.

The Clinical Classifications

Acute Stress Disorder and Posttraumatic Stress Disorder

The two major diagnoses associated with exposure to a traumatic incident are Acute Stress Disorder (ASD) and Posttraumatic Stress Disorder (PTSD) (APA, 2000). Both are found within the classification known as "Anxiety Disorders" because their main features include symptoms of anxiety and avoidant behaviors, but they differ from other anxiety disorders in that the predominant symptom is not anxiety but rather a re-experiencing of the traumatic incident through intrusive recollections, flashbacks, or nightmares.

In both ASD and PTSD, a person must have experienced, witnessed, or been presented with an event involving physical injury or threat to oneself or another person. This can be as intense as being tortured or as remote as hearing about a loved one being kidnapped or killed. In all cases, and regardless of the level of exposure, at the time of the trauma the person will have experienced a sense of terror, horror, or helplessness: feelings that will be re-experienced again and again in the days, months, or even years following the trauma.

Some have described PTSD as being in a "survival mode" and being unable to return to normal (Volkmann, 2003). In order to receive a diagnosis of either ASD or PTSD following the traumatic event, the person must experience symptoms along three main dimensions: in-trusion, avoidance, and arousal. The types of symp-toms are very similar for the two diagnoses, but ASD requires fewer avoidance symptoms and may involve a sense of numbing or feelings of depersonalization (feel-ing detached or estranged from your own experiences) or derealization (a change in your experience of the world, where normal things feel unreal, unfamiliar, or ar-tificial). But the main factor that delineates one diagnosis from the other is time. ASD basically refers to the initial symptom response, the one that occurs within the first month and lasts for a minimum of two days. PTSD refers to the symptoms that last for more than one month. In other words, a person's ASD can become PTSD if the symptoms worsen and continue for more than one month or begin several months after the initial incident (called "delayed onset").

As mentioned previously, the main feature of ASD and PTSD is that the trauma is persistently re-experi-enced or, in some extreme cases, re-lived. This can occur through intrusive thoughts or images associated with the event. For example, a firefighter who recov-ered a badly burned body of a child from a house fire may still "smell" the burnt skin, "see" the child's black-ened face, or "feel" the weight of the child in their arms days or even weeks after the event. Maybe every time they see a child, they cannot help but think of the child who died in the fire. Or every time a call comes in at work, they think of the call involving the child. Thoughts of the child in the incident may even be transferred to the firefighter's own children, causing over-protective-ness or the inability to sleep at night for fear that their own house may catch fire.

One very common way that the memories of the trauma will be re-experienced is through dreams. Sometimes the event will be "remembered" and the person's nightmares will be as if they were re-living the incident. Other times the details will be altered or less clear, but the feelings produced during the dream will be the same. A firefighter who was involved with the events of September 11 may have dreams filled with images of doomed, faceless people or the choking sensation from trying to breathe the thick dust and smoke-filled air.

The second symptom area is avoidance, which refers to the person's engaging in efforts to avoid reminders of the incident. Avoidance behaviors may include refusing to talk about the incident or avoiding places or people associated with the trauma. A firefighter involved in a traumatic incident may drive out of their way in an effort to avoid an intersection where they saw a gruesome car accident or may always change the topic if someone starts to talk about the incident. In some cases a person may be unable to recall aspects of the trauma, as if the brain had erased part of the memory. Feelings of detachment or estrangement or a decreased interest in significant activities are also symptoms associated with avoidance. These behaviors represent efforts to avoid thinking about the traumatic event and minimize the anxiety associated with it. Many times the avoidance is not a conscious action. The person may not even be aware that they are avoiding reminders of the trauma and may come up with other explanations for changing their path to work, or no longer wanting to have scanners in the house, or not wanting to work with certain crew mates or on a certain apparatus.

Arousal, the third type of symptom found in PTSD

and ASD, refers to a heightened state of anxiety that may present itself in a variety of areas. Oftentimes the anxiety makes it difficult for a person to fall asleep or stay asleep (especially if the person has had recurrent nightmares). Heightened anxiety may also interfere with a person's ability to concentrate, making a normally detail-oriented person appear careless. One of the hallmark symptoms of someone experiencing increased arousal is an exaggerated startle response, where the slightest noise or action sends a person's system into a state of alarm. For a normally happy, outgoing person, the experience of intense, chronic anxiety can turn them into someone who is now angry, irritable, and "on the edge" all the time, confusing friends and family and driving away the very people who most want to help.

For both ASD and PTSD, the symptoms must cause distress to the person experiencing them and interfere with normal social or occupational functioning. The firefighter experiencing PTSD may find that their marriage is suffering because of their anger and irritability or that they have quickly depleted their reserve of sick-days in an attempt to avoid work-related reminders of the trauma. In this way the symptoms travel far beyond the person who actually experienced the trauma, affecting the people in the social network as well. In many cases it will not even be the person suffering from the PTSD or ASD who finally decides that professional help is needed; it will be the firefighter's boss, or best friend, or spouse, or even their child. These "other" affected people will decide that they can no longer watch their loved one live in pain or ruin their career and will give them an ultimatum: get help or else... .

In order to confirm a diagnosis of ASD or PTSD,

clinicians may combine their clinical assessment of the person taken during a series of interviews with results from a psychological test instrument (Warley, 2004). Different types of clinicians will favor different types of psychological scales, but some of the more commonly used scales include the Structured Clinical Interview for DSM (SCID) and the Minnesota Multiphasic Personality Inventory (MMPI-II). More psychodynamic clinicians may even use the Rorschach (ink-blot test). The clinician will then compare their own clinical impressions and the test results with various diagnostic criteria before coming up with a diagnosis. Often they will also want to rule out the possibility that the person's psychological symptoms are the result of a psychoactive substance (especially for ASD) or an organic illness, such as dementia.

Other Disorders Commonly Associated with PTSD

According to the Executive Director of the National Center for PTSD (Friedman, 2003), someone who meets the diagnostic criteria for PTSD is also likely to be diagnosed with one or more additional disorders. The most common "co-morbid" psychological disorders include affective disorders, such as major depression, and substance-related disorders, such as drug or alcohol abuse or dependence (Everly & Lating, 2004; Frideman, 2001; Green & Kaltman, 2003). These other problems usually develop as the result of the traumatic experience. Individuals may become depressed about feeling disconnected from their career (and their identity as a firefighter) or may turn to drugs or alcohol in an attempt to block out intrusive images or reduce the feelings of overwhelming anxiety. Ironically enough, it may be these secondary disorders that ultimately bring the person suffering from PTSD to the attention of a mental health professional. The chief of the department may turn the other way when the issue is excessive use of sick-time but draw the line when the firefighter shows up at work smelling of alcohol.

Depression

Major Depressive Disorder is more commonly diagnosed in women, but it is still estimated that 1 in 14 men will experience depression at some time in their lives (Hales & Hales, 2004). Symptoms of depression can include depressed mood, a loss of interest or pleasure in previously enjoyable activities, significant changes in appetite and weight, difficulty sleeping, fatigue, difficulty concentrating, either restlessness or slowness of movements, feelings of worthlessness or inappropriate guilt, and thoughts of suicide (APA, 2000). In order to receive a diagnosis of Major Depressive Disorder, these symptoms must be present for 2 weeks or longer and either produce significant distress to the individual or impair social or occupational functioning.

37

Major depression goes far beyond just feeling "blue" or "down in the dumps," although that is often how people describe their mood when they are feeling depressed. It is a mood that is both pervasive and intense, and it permeates a person's whole outlook on life. It makes it hard to look forward to tomorrow, let alone see any kind of hope in the future. There are several symptoms that overlap between PTSD and Major Depressive Disorder, including a loss of interest in activities, sleep disturbance, and memory impairment. And it is easy to see how a firefighter's tendency to assume responsibility for things that are out of their control could lead to feelings of inappropriate guilt. A firefighter who experienced a "bad call," and who blames himself for the negative outcome, could easily develop Major Depressive Disorder in addition to PTSD.

The most dangerous aspect of major depression concerns thoughts of suicide. Many people who are depressed think of suicide, at least briefly, and someone who has considered suicide may be willing to try it. A firefighter or fire officer who feels responsible for the death or injury of another firefighter (even if the guilt is inappropriate) may find that thoughts of suicide creep into their mind, making it seem as if suicide were a form of atonement.

As mentioned previously, women are more likely than men to be diagnosed with depression. They are also more likely to attempt suicide or make a suicidal gesture (considered to be a "cry for help" rather than a genuine attempt to end their own life). Men, on the other hand, are more like to successfully commit suicide if they try, partly because they tend to choose more lethal means, such as firearms or hanging. If you think that someone you know may be contemplating committing suicide, do not be afraid to talk to them about your concerns. Contrary to some beliefs, you will not increase the likelihood that the person will commit suicide. By asking them about it, you are demonstrating your concern for their welfare, and you can offer them alternatives that the narrow, tunnel-like thinking of depression may have kept from their minds. Talk of suicide should always be taken seriously. It is a sign of ultimate desperation and desperate people cannot think clearly. (For additional resources on depression or suicide please see Appendix C.)

Substance Abuse or Dependency

Those who are tormented with disturbing memories or crippling anxiety may find that they are so desperate to dull the pain that they will turn to drugs or alcohol for relief. Even though the relief may be temporary and the substance use may end up causing even further disruption in the person's life, it may feel worth it to have a few hours of mental numbing. Drug- or alcohol-related problems that may be found in someone with PTSD include substance abuse or substance dependence.

A person will be diagnosed with substance abuse if they continue to use a psychoactive substance despite the knowledge that it is causing them physical problems or difficulties in their social relationships or occupational roles, or if they continue to use in physically hazardous situations (such as while operating a vehicle). Going to a bar and drinking alcohol would not constitute abuse. Neither would drinking to the point of physical illness, if it only occurred once or twice. But regularly drinking to the point of physical illness or driving while intoxicated (with the behaviors repeatedly occurring for a month or longer) would be classified as "abuse."

Substance dependence is considered a more serious disorder than abuse. Symptoms of dependence include behavioral changes in which the person

- has built up a tolerance to the substance,
- requires larger and larger amounts to achieve the same effects over a period of time,
- wants to or has tried unsuccessfully in the past to stop using,
- expends a great deal of effort in either obtaining,

using, or recovering from the substance,
- is frequently intoxicated or in withdrawal when expected to perform other roles,
- has given up other social or occupational activities in order to use,
- continues to use despite the resulting social or occupational problems, and/or
- experiences withdrawal or continues using to avoid withdrawal.

Abuse may lead to dependence, especially for highly addictive substances such as opioids (e.g., heroin) and nicotine. Someone who self-medicates with marijuana or heroin to control feelings of anxiety may, in fact, get some temporary relief and therefore be more likely to use again in the future. Although use of the drug may start out on a sporadic basis, relieving the symptoms only when they have become unbearable, the person may eventually find themselves addicted to the drug and be unable to get through a day without using.

Obviously some substances are considered more serious than others. People might feel sorry for you if you are addicted to caffeine or nicotine, and they may worry about you if you have an alcohol problem, but at least these substances are legal. An emergency worker who uses illegal drugs or who steals painkillers from the ambulance is not only risking health but also freedom and career if caught. And while people may be sympathetic concerning one's PTSD, they are less likely to be sympathetic to substance use or dependence, blaming the drug use on personal weakness rather then viewing it as an attempt to block out intrusive, painful memories.

Traumatic Stress in Firefighters

Knowing what we know about firefighters and their jobs, one can clearly see that many of them are likely to be affected by traumatic stress at some point in their careers. But just how likely is it that a firefighter will experience a stress-related injury? Surprisingly enough, that question is very difficult to answer.

Trauma Rates (Nationally and Internationally)

Although work-related injuries in the United States should be reported to the National Institute for Occupational Safety and Health (NIOSH), many firefighters who experience a traumatic stress injury may not report it for fear that it will be viewed as a sign of personal weakness or that it will negatively impact their potential for promotion. Others may be identified as having difficulties associated with exposure to trauma, but rather than claim a psychological injury, may take an early retirement. Or, if they were physically injured as well, they may go out on a physical, rather than psychological, disability. Neither the National Fire Protection Association (NFPA) nor the International Association of Firefighters (IAFF) currently collect data on the number of firefighters who have experienced stress-related injuries, but among IAFF members, 6.8% of all line of duty disability retirements were attributed to "mental stress" (IAFF, 2000). Unfortunately, IAFF membership only represents a small percentage of firefighters in the United States, so it is unclear how representative these figures may be.

41

Two years after the terror attacks of September 11, *The Wall Street Journal* (September 8, 2003) published an article examining emergency personnel involved in rescue and recovery operations in New York City. The article reported PTSD rates of nearly 19% among the workers at Ground Zero. But PTSD rates at this level are not solely associated with firefighters involved in large-scale disasters, nor are they limited to firefighters in the United States.

PTSD can be found among firefighters all over the world, from urban to rural, volunteer to professional. Taylor (1995) found that over 80% of fire officers in the British Fire Service had experienced one or more PTSD symptoms at some point in their careers. Of those who reported symptoms, nearly one third indicated that the symptoms had lasted for a prolonged period of time, taking years to diminish in some cases. In Germany, Wagner and colleagues (1998) identified a PTSD symptom rate of 18.2% among professional firefighters, nearly identical to the PTSD symptom rate described by Al-Naser and Everly (1999) among Kuwaiti firefighters (18.5%). Similarly, Australian firefighters sampled reported experiencing psychological distress rates ranging from 16% to 24%, depending on the type of firefighter (Dean, Gow, & Shakespeare-Finch, 2003). Their research compared traumatic stress symptomatology levels in career firefighters with those of auxiliary (volunteer) firefighters. Higher rates of psychological distress were observed among the career firefighters, and the number of years that a firefighter had on the job was positively associated with the level of distress reported; (i.e., more experienced personnel had higher psychological symptom levels). When these figures are compared with PTSD rates of 7% to 9% in the general population (APA, 2000), it becomes evident that firefighters constitute a special population in need of prevention, regular screening, and early intervention services.

Long-term Impact of Traumatic Stress

In addition to the upsetting and problematic symptoms of ASD and PTSD that you read about earlier in the chapter, the trauma experienced by a firefighter may be compounded with other, more common job-related stressors, and the cumulative, long-term impact of all these stressors will take both a personal and a professional toll (see Figure 3-1). Some of the long-term effects of these stressors include continued memory problems, a decreased ability to make decisions, difficulty attending to the environment, mental instability, interpersonal conflicts, alcoholism, depression, and possibly even suicide. North and colleagues (2002) found that changes in relationships were reported by nearly half of the firefighters in their sample who had PTSD (42%) as compared with 13% among those without PTSD.

43

And because these problems affect firefighters, they will also have a negative impact on their departments. Personal problems become work-related problems such as decreased performance, proneness to accidents, decreased morale, chronic absenteeism, high medical costs, and increased staff turn-over as the result of higher than normal rates of attrition and early retirement (FEMA, 1991). Neely and Spitzer (1997) state, "Stress among emergency workers may reduce performance to the extent of endangering both the professionals and civilians at an emergency scene" (p. 114).

Figure 3-1

Cumulative and Long-Term Effects of Stress

Personal

- Memory impairment
- Difficulty making decisions
- Difficulty attending to the environment
- Mental instability
- Interpersonal conflicts
- Alcoholism
- Depression
- Suicide

Departmental Problems

- Decreased performance
- Proneness to accidents
- Decreased morale
- Chronic absenteeism
- High medical costs
- Increased staff turn-over

Source: *Stress Management: Model Program for Maintaining Firefighter Well-Being,* Federal Emergency Management Agency, US Fire Administration, February 1991.

Many supervisors and fire chiefs will probably find that they spend a great deal of time addressing personal problems rather than technical problems. In a personal correspondence, the Chief of the Nantucket (MA) Fire Department stated, "We call ourselves professionals. Most professionals I know seek help from their colleagues, from other sources and know when to seek personal assistance" (E. Pierce, June 21, 2004).

Areas for Future Researchers

More needs to be known regarding the short- and llong-term effects of traumatic stress on firefighters, and once it is known, programs need to be developed and implemented in order to prevent (whenever possible) and mitigate (to the fullest extent) its effects. As the diagnostic criteria concerning traumatic stress changes, so too will the number of firefighters who meet that criteria. Since the diagnostic criteria for ASD are less stringent, and the exposure of firefighters to trauma is so great, we might expect to see higher rates of ASD among firefighters, but only if the trauma is actually reported. In order for this to happen, the cultural acceptance of traumatic stress within the fire service must change so that it is considered to be a valid injury, no different from an injured back or shoulder.

We need a better understanding of how best to help a firefighter get through and recover from traumatic stress, especially when it has developed into PTSD. Removing a firefighter from the fire service is equivalent to taking away that firefighter's identity and can only make it more difficult to "return to normal." More also needs to be known about how traumatic stress impacts volunteer firefighters as compared to career firefighters and how the two groups may differ in terms of crisis intervention service needs.

It is equally important to remember that a majority of firefighters, though exposed to serious death and injury, will not develop PTSD, and that those who do develop PTSD are likely to recover if they receive timely, professional assistance (Tucker, 1995). At present, we have no way of knowing who will get PTSD and who will not. Until we can accurately predict an individual firefighter's likelihood of developing PTSD, we should assume that nearly one fifth of our personnel may develop PTSD, and we should engage in appropriate, departmental-wide prevention efforts in order to assist as many of them as possible.

In Summary

Diagnostic criteria for PTSD have evolved over the years as our understanding of psychological trauma has grown. This chapter described the diagnoses commonly associated with traumatic experience: Postttraumatic Stress Disorder and Acute Stress Disorder. Both diagnoses result from a threat of death or serious injury and involve symptoms of intrusion, avoidance, and arousal. People who have experienced a traumatic stress disorder are also often at risk for depression and drug- or alcohol-related problems. While we know that firefighters are a special population at increased risk for developing PTSD and that the long-term negative effects of traumatic stress are numerous, we are unable to predict who will develop PTSD. More research needs to be done to better understand, effectively mitigate, and (ideally) prevent traumatic stress reactions among firefighters.

Chapter Four

Case #1
Car Fire

On October 6, 1999, at 12:57 a.m., the phone rang at the home of a young fire investigator named Mike. On the line was the dispatcher, requesting that he respond to the scene of a reported car accident/fire on a major interstate highway. The call seemed fairly straightforward to Mike at the time and, before responding to the accident scene, he first drove to the station to pick up the inspector's vehicle and his investigation equipment.

As Mike drove from the station to the scene he thought to himself how refreshing the cool night air felt on his face after being awakened from a sound sleep. Mike also began running down the mental checklist of what he might expect to find once he arrived. He figured that he would find one of two scenarios: either an accidental or an incendiary vehicle fire. Mike's job was to determine what came first, the accident or the fire, and to try to determine how the fire had started. Mike felt fortunate that he was able to go directly to the scene of the vehicle fire, thereby decreasing the likelihood of losing valuable evidence, which he knew often happened once a vehicle was moved from the scene.

As soon as Mike arrived on scene he began to size up the situation and compile notes concerning his initial observations. Two different fire departments and three different law enforcement agencies had responded to the call. The car was still off the road approximately 50 feet, where it was entangled in a large oak tree, still smoldering from the freshly extinguished flames.

Mike was greeted by the fire chief and was informed that he was clear to begin his investigation concerning the fatal crash. This comment took Mike by surprise. To this point, no one had mentioned that there was a victim involved, much less a deceased victim.

The State Police had discovered a badly burned female body on the ground next to the car. Mike quickly realized that he now had a more important question to answer, "Was she dead before being burned or did she die as the result of her burns?" He knew that a majority of fire deaths do not result from the flames but rather from the smoke. There was also the possibility that someone had put the woman's body in the car and set it on fire in order to hide a crime. Regardless, the death involved had created additional steps for the fire investigator. Mike also knew that he would need to work closely with the law enforcement agencies on the case, at least until arson or some other crime had been ruled out. (In Mike's state, the fire department is responsible for determining the cause and origin of the fire and the police department becomes involved if there is a crime, such as arson or homicide.)

After working at the scene for about 40 minutes, the State Medical Examiners Office (SMEO) representative arrived to remove the body from the scene. The SMEO was responsible for conducting the medical examination of the deceased person, and the information provided by Mike would help him make sense of the autopsy results. The attendant from the SMEO asked the fire chief if he had permission to remove the body from the scene and was informed that all necessary sketches and photographs had been taken and that the body could be "bagged."

The fire chief asked Mike to help the medical examiner with the procedure. Involving Mike in the removal of the body was done to provide the investigator with a "chain of evidence," permitting him to witness first hand when and how the body was moved and by whom. Helping move the body was also important because it would provide the fire investigator with an opportunity to view the underside of the body, as well as the condition of the ground, clothing, and the skin.

Mike had been around burned bodies before and knew that the smell was going to be rough. Burned human flesh has a very distinctive smell—a smell that people say you will never forget. In fact, most fire investigators will tell you that the smell almost seems to permeate your hair follicles and your skin and that no amount of soap can get rid of it.

The medical examiner and Mike walked over to the body and began to stretch out a body bag on the ground next to it. Mike was at the head and the medical examiner was at the feet. The body was lying face down and Mike could clearly see that the lower half of the body had extensive damage to the soft tissue with less severe burns on the victim's head. When the first firefighters had arrived on scene, the car had been totally engulfed in flames. The victim's body was found about 4 feet away. It appeared that the intense heat generated by the fire had caused the body to burn, since the part of the victim's body that was closest to the car (her feet) had sustained the most damage.

Mike had been investigating fires for more than six

49

years and had conducted several fire death investigations. In his mind, this one should not have been any different. However, as he and the medical examiner rolled over the nineteen-year-old female body, Mike found himself staring directly into the woman's open eyes. "It seemed as if she was looking right at me," recalled Mike. The experience was brief, but the image was to stay with him for years to come.

Mike and the person from the SMEO put the body in a bag and moved it onto a stretcher and into the back of the medical examiner's vehicle. All the while Mike could not shake the disturbing image and the thought that the girl had been looking right into his eyes.

Three hours into the incident, Mike decided that he had completed his field investigation. Having only a couple of hours of the night left, he returned home to get some much needed sleep before returning to work the next day. At home he took a shower and changed into clean clothes, but he could still smell the distinctive odor of burned flesh. Even worse than the smell were the thoughts racing through his mind as he tried to sleep that night.

After the Incident

The next day, Mike met with the police investigator to compare notes and thoughts about the accident and death and to begin writing his initial report on the fire. Later that afternoon, Mike spoke with the fire chief about the incident and, during the course of the conversation, mentioned to the chief that he had not been able to get the face of the victim out of his mind. The fire chief said, "I've had times when calls stuck with me, too. But after some time, they usually go away." The chief asked Mike if he would like to speak with someone about how he was feeling. Mike thanked the chief but declined any assistance and continued on with his job.

During the next few weeks Mike's behavior dramatically changed: he avoided work, refused to take on any additional shifts at the station, and no longer completed his reports in a timely fashion. He was spending more and more time away from the community and would regularly retreat to his camp, several hours away. When Mike got paged out for a fire investigation, he would refuse the assignment, giving the excuse that he was too far away to respond. It was becoming obvious to everyone that he was avoiding calls and that his work was beginning to suffer. However, when the fire chief questioned him about his absenteeism, he always had an excuse.

From Trouble to PTSD

Sarah, Mike's girlfriend, remarked that it was not just his work that suffered following the incident. His health was also in a definite downward spiral. "He was not eating right, he was not sleeping, and he had an extremely high level of anxiety," Sarah recalled. Since the night of the car fire Mike had been regularly experiencing nightmares. He found that he would get a couple of hours of sleep and then be awakened by a recurrent nightmare that consisted of faceless people chasing him. "Mike wouldn't talk about the nightmares. If I pushed him for information about the dreams it just made him very uncomfortable," said Sarah. After being wakened by the dreams, Mike would be unable to get back to sleep, which meant that he was suffering from insomnia in addition to the intrusive images.

Another marked change in Mike's behavior concerned cigar smoking. He had never been much of a smoker before the car fire incident, but since then he had started to smoke small cigars, and if he was not smoking the cigar, he was chewing on it. It seemed as if he always had a cigar hanging out of his mouth. But while the nicotine may have contributed to his feelings of agitation, it was obviously not the primary source of his anxiety.

By November, just one month after the call, Mike had lost more than 40 pounds from not eating, and he hated seeing people from the fire station. In fact, he avoided anything having to do with the fire department. No news. No friends from the station. No reminders. Eventually, Mike made an appointment to speak with his family doctor about the changes going on in his life. After describing his symptoms to the doctor, Mike was placed on a medical disability and prescribed medication to reduce his anxiety but was not referred to a therapist for treatment.

Two months later, with the aid of the anti-anxiety medication, Mike was cleared to return to full duty at the fire station. He had managed to control many of his symptoms, but he was still far from his old self. Most of his co-workers at the station, however, had no idea of the psychological pain he continued to experience on a daily basis. Since the night of the car fire, Mike had not received any psychological assistance other than the prescription from his primary physician and had not spoken with anyone about the incident or the symptoms he had been experiencing.

Over the next seven months there were even more

changes in Mike's personality and behaviors. He had always been a happy, easy-going person, but he had become very aggressive and easily provoked. His sleep habits changed from too little sleep (right after the incident) to too much, with Mike sleeping between 16 and 18 hours per day. He also avoided leaving the house and lost interest in most of the things he used to enjoy. He was like an entirely different person, depressed and angry, and his girlfriend, Sarah, watched the dramatic change but felt helpless to intervene.

Again, it was Mike's family doctor who was finally contacted and informed of the problematic symptoms. At that point, he switched Mike off of the original antianxiety medication and put him on an antidepressant. In an attempt to further dull the symptoms, Mike increased his alcohol consumption despite the warnings concerning the hazards of mixing alcohol with antidepressant medications. "At one point it just didn't matter what time of day it was. He would open up a beer at eight o'clock in the morning. He just wanted to take the edge off," said Sarah.

In the year that followed the car fire incident Mike struggled to manage his symptoms until finally his level of anxiety and agitation became overwhelming. Anything and everything associated with the fire service became a trigger for him. He would become upset whenever he heard sirens, saw accidents on the roadside, watched media coverage of fires and accidents, or even overheard conversations about the fire service. Mike eventually removed all of the fire department radios from his house and shop, but he was still unable to escape from reminders of the accident scene and the trauma he was trying to block out. In August 2001, Mike was

53

once again placed on medical leave from the fire department and real help was finally on the way.

Search for Support

That August Mike was diagnosed with PTSD and clinical depression and began to receive treatment from a psychologist. His medications were adjusted to better control his symptoms, and he began weekly psychotherapy sessions. For Mike, this was the very first time he had spoken in any detail about the incident and the way it had devastated his life. And, although Mike's family had heard about Posttraumatic Stress Disorder, they had very little knowledge of it and considered PTSD a problem associated with soldiers and wars, not with firefighters. The idea that Mike could have been traumatized to the point of developing PTSD took him and his family completely by surprise.

The diagnosis also took the town by surprise. The town's first response was to reject the on-the-job injury claim, even though in Mike's case the injury could be narrowed down to one, specific incident. The town's insurance policy stated that for PTSD, "...treatment must be recommended by a legally qualified physician and received within 60 days of the date of participation in the emergency duty." In other words, Mike should have been diagnosed within the two months following the incident in order for the town to consider the claim. They were not willing to accept a delayed diagnosis of PTSD, refused to grant Mike a line-of-duty injury status, and initially made him use his sick time.

A couple of weeks later, the town ordered Mike to the town doctor (a psychologist) for a psychological evaluation. The town doctor did not initially believe that Mike had been sufficiently injured by his work but eventually did concur with the diagnosis of PTSD. The doctor further stated it was too soon to determine if Mike's injury was permanent.

Mike felt as if his life was suddenly under a microscope and that everything he did was being scrutinized: by the town, by his fellow firefighters, and by his friends and family. He was dealing with a high degree of guilt and was angry that some people actually thought he was faking the PTSD in order to get out on a disability.

The rumors and suspicions concerning Mike's injury claim served to drive him away from some of the very people who could have helped him the most at that time: his fellow firefighters and even the fire department chaplain. The department's chaplain also happened to be the pastor of Mike's church. He had known Mike for many years, had stopped by to visit after Mike had been injured falling off a roof, and had been a particularly good source of support following the death of Mike's father. But, despite their positive personal history together, the fire chaplain was nowhere to be seen when Mike was at his lowest point, plagued by anxiety and alienated from his department. For Mike, this was perhaps the most painful lack of support that he experienced at the time.

Without a doubt, Mike's main support came from his immediate family, who attempted to be supportive and understanding, as they themselves struggled to understand what he was dealing with. His girlfriend regularly drove him to therapy each week, 50 minutes each way. Having Sarah present provided him with someone to talk to during the drive and helped keep him from further closing Sarah off from what he was going through. "His support was in his house. This was the only place he got the support he needed," said Sarah. However, on several occasions they had a total breakdown in communications resulting in some very difficult times. At points, it would have been very easy just to quit and walk away from the relationship, but that was not what either of them wanted. And, in the end, they both felt that it made their relationship much stronger. "We both wanted the same thing, we just didn't know how to get there," said Sarah.

It is interesting to note that Sarah had many of the same feelings of anger and betrayal concerning the town that Mike experienced, just at a much lower level. She blamed the department for being responsible for his PTSD and for not doing anything to help him after the incident.

Mike's Epilogue

Today, with the help of a healthy combination of medication and psychotherapy, Mike is able to manage his PTSD and depression. "You never get over it [PTSD], you live your life with it and manage the symptoms," said Sarah of his experience. Since being diagnosed with PTSD, Mike and his family have tried to educate themselves as much as possible about the disorder, a tactic that can help someone feel more in control of their illness as they select their course of treatment and learn what to expect in the future.

Over the past couple of years, Mike has built up a tolerance to several medications used to treat his PTSD. His doctor has had to monitor his medication closely and make several changes. In the fall of 2001, Mike's psychologist requested a full medical work-up in order to rule out any underlying medical conditions that may or may not have impacted his course of treatment. At that point, his medication slate was wiped cleaned and a whole new set of medications were prescribed.

For Mike, being out of work was like a double-edged sword. The positive aspect for him was being able to get away from the stimuli and just focus on his own recovery. The downside, however, was that taking a medical leave pulled him away from a potential source of support (his co-workers) and led to speculations that he was malingering. In the time following the car fire incident, Mike's mood had been somewhat unstable. "His mood was like a roller coaster. He had high points and then his mood would come speeding down to a low point," commented Sarah. The mood swings seemed to diminish almost entirely after he received word of his disability retirement from the department. For Mike, it was as if others had finally accepted the fact that his injury was real, thereby validating his experience and permitting him finally to move on.

Some three years after the car fire incident, Mike is still in therapy and managing his symptoms. "He's a willing participant and very vocal about stuff that bothers him now," said Sarah, "But this wasn't always the case." She feels that Mike may never completely recover from PTSD but, at least for now, he has regained much of the control of his life that he lost after the incident.

Mike cannot even begin to think about what would have happened if he had not reached out for help. He and his family members all agree that the end result would have been much different. "There is absolutely no question in my mind that therapy saved his life," said Sarah. She admitted, "It took a long time for him to realize that he needed it, but once he did, it was the best thing for him. Seeking help, regardless of how minor it may seem to you, is very important in the long run. Knowing that there is help out there, someone to turn to before you lose it, is just so important." Sarah emphasized, "Don't be embarrassed if you're experiencing a stress response from a call. After all, you didn't bring it on yourself. Let your family know what you're going through and how they can help. It doesn't have to be a secret."

Chapter 5

Case #2
World Trade Center
Assistance

September 11, 2001, changed so many lives forever, including the life of Firefighter Adam. The world watched the events unfold on television or listened to it on the radio, but others witnessed it first hand. As the Fire Department of New York (FDNY) responded to this tragic event, the call went out for assistance from Critical Incident Stress Management (CISM) teams from across the country. Adam's CISM team, located in another large city, was one of the many to respond to the call.

On September 14, Adam, along with several other firefighters from his CISM team, headed out to New York City by car because all of the airports were still closed. As they entered the city, their attention was drawn to the large, gaping hole in the city skyline: the hole left when the twin towers of the World Trade Center collapsed three days earlier.

On Saturday, September 15, Adam and his team assembled as a united group and traveled to Ground Zero. After numerous delays in obtaining clearance and establishing communication with the right people, the team was finally given their assignment around 7:30 p.m. "Going down there, I just couldn't put into words what I was thinking about and expecting. I couldn't describe it in my mind," recalled Adam. Before entering

Ground Zero, the team was given a brief description of what they would be encountering at the site. After the instruction, they were brought to the heart of Ground Zero and given an opportunity to walk around the area and see first-hand the level of destruction that had occurred.

As they walked into the area, floodlights illuminated the devastation. "I'll never forget the floodlights, the eeriness, smoke still rising, and the smell. Just walking into it was like walking into a nuclear scenario: the people walking around, the weird taste in the atmosphere, all the shit in the air floating down. It's just hard to describe," said Adam. No one was capable of explaining what the team was about to face.

During the two-hour tour of Ground Zero, the team witnessed with their own eyes what many of us never got to see on TV. "Everywhere we walked you would see something that was incomprehensible," said Adam. Members of the team with years in the fire service were amazed at what they witnessed. Some things they could not even make out, like being in a smoked-filled room.

By one account, the flying ash had blanketed the area like a fresh coating of winter snow, distorting the sights and muffling the sounds, enhancing the surrealistic feeling that many experienced while working there. "Looking around you would see women's shoes lying on the ground and not recognize the buildings around you. It was just debris, dust, and steel everywhere," said Adam. As they walked around Ground Zero they took great care, because the next step could be on top of a body part. Initially, it was not unusual to travel a short distance and find some body part sticking out from beneath a pile of wreckage.

The CISM team was assigned to the American Express building because everyone who traveled to the morgue had to travel through that area. "The morgue was about 40 feet from us. The smell of the bodies is something that I will never forget," remembered Adam. "No one will ever be able to truly put into words what we saw and smelled and tasted there."

Adam was assigned to provide peer-support to the fire crews. He and his team worked 12-hour shifts, during which time they had contact with many of the people who passed through the area, bringing bodies and body parts to the morgue. Adam recalled how difficult it was to determine how people were coping with the stress. "Just to gauge how someone was doing was very hard. It was so new, nothing like this had ever happened before. It was hard psychologically to read what was going on," said Adam. Individuals and groups of people from all backgrounds of crisis management and other areas of psychology had been showing up, offering their assistance. "Everyone was muscling for a piece of the pie," said Adam.

The streets around Ground Zero contained destroyed fire and police vehicles, crushed by the fallen buildings. It had been reported that more than 25 fire engines, 30 ladder trucks, and more than 35 command vehicles were buried when the towers collapsed. For Adam, the number of emergency vehicles that had been destroyed would serve as a reminder of the evil that had taken place.

When Adam's first 12-hour shift came to an end he felt as if he had been there for a week. "When I was walking out of the site, I was walking back up West Side Highway, my thoughts were 'I wish I'd never come here.'

If I'd known that it was going to be that bad, I would have never put myself into that position. I just wouldn't have done it. I don't care. I don't think anyone in the world was strong enough to handle what they were seeing," confessed Adam. But he knew that he was there for a purpose, and he was determined not to let down the people of New York or his fellow firefighters, and so he stayed.

Each day, at the end of their shift, Adam and the others would return to their hotel. But even there, it was impossible to get away from the mission. "When we came back to the hotel, all we would do is talk with people about what they'd been doing there that day. It was a constant 24-hour barrage of Ground Zero. You couldn't get away from it," he said. And the constant talk about what each worker had experienced meant that Adam and the other team members never had any real "downtime," even during the hours spent off-site. The process continued non-stop for Adam and his team during the entire time they worked at Ground Zero: six long weeks.

During Adam's first week of work, one particular incident stood out in his mind. After several days of no aircraft in the air, a jet took off from Newark Airport flying over the work area, and everything went silent. "Everyone was working in the pit, but when the jet took off from the airport, all of a sudden, you could hear a pin drop. Everyone just totally stopped working. It was eerie," Adam remembered in vivid detail.

Another incident that stuck in Adam's mind was the day they found a number of victims in one location. The smell of the dead bodies was horrendous, but even more disturbing to Adam than the smell was the sight of all those body bags coming through the building that day.

During the first couple of weeks, Adam took his camera with him into Ground Zero. Little did he know at the time that he would be unable to look at those photos when he returned home, nor could he understand just how central those pictures would be to his healing and recovery a few years later.

After the first week on scene, it was decided that Adam's team would break into groups of three and go around to the area fire stations. Each group consisted of a peer mediator, a chaplain, and a member of the CISM team. "The peer mediator was from New York City and most of the time he was a retired guy who had the instant respect," said Adam. "We would talk to the firefighters who had been down at Ground Zero. We would try and gauge where they were, psychologically. We'd hear story after story after story after story about how they were feeling, about what they witnessed, about who got killed. But a lot of times the guys were reluctant to talk to anyone at all. They were angry."

Adam worked on the three-person team visiting fire stations for the next three weeks, with his time off monopolized in much the same way back at the hotel, talking about the day's events with others. The crushing weight was not like a ton of bricks falling on Adam's head, but rather like having one brick at a time placed on his shoulders every minute that he was there. Not sudden, but crushing none the less.

After six weeks Adam finally returned home to his wife and his job, burdened by the new weight that he carried, physically and mentally exhausted.

After The Incident

Returning home did not mean returning to normal for Adam, although he tried to ease himself back into the life he knew before September 11. He and his wife took a long needed vacation to Hawaii. "I was sitting on the beach, looking at the water and all I could think about was planes crashing into the water," said Adam. "I was fixated with jets taking off. Once I saw a jet take off, I immediately flashed back to New York, the ash, soot and shit floating down on my uniform. I thought I was going crazy, but I didn't tell anyone."

Back home, Adam's fixation with jets became more and more intrusive. One day, while he was driving down the highway, he saw a jet plane taking off from the airport and became fixated on the plane. He was so focused on the plane that he stopped paying attention to the road ahead of him, the lane of traffic he was in, and the speed he was going, and he nearly caused an accident. Another time, while working at fire headquarters, Adam was leaving the building when he noticed a jet plane taking off from the airport. This time he became so fixated on the jet plane that he didn't notice that he had walked straight into traffic. Cars were honking their horns, people were yelling at him, and it took him several seconds to realize what he had done.

According to one of his friends, Adam came home from Ground Zero a changed man. Before his experience, he was a physically fit young man who ran marathons and worked out regularly at the gym. Socially, Adam was always an upbeat, positive person. After returning from Ground Zero, he was completely different: not active, isolating himself from his friends, and very negative about everything around him.

From Trouble to PTSD

"I don't know exactly when I developed PTSD," said Adam. "I was depressed. I lost my marriage over it. I was isolating myself. I didn't want to go out. And I couldn't watch anything having to do with New York on TV. I just slowly declined to a point where I couldn't take it anymore. Even my wife was fed up with me. I had an extramarital affair, because, . . . I don't know why. When you're in the middle of it all, you think you're worthless and that your marriage is going down the tubes, so you just don't care about anything anymore. I even called the fire department and told the stress unit coordinator that I wanted to quit," said Adam.

Over the course of the next year, Adam's feelings of depression increased and his marriage disintegrated, but he continued to function on the job. Even that changed, however, one day in March, 2003. While working his normal shift at the fire station that day, a call came in for a "strange odor" inside a building. "I was the 'open-up man' on the truck and when we went in, there was a dead guy on the floor. He'd been dead for a couple of days. And all of a sudden that smell and that taste and everything about that scene brought me right back to New York City," recalled Adam.

Somehow he managed to struggle through the flood of emotions at the scene, but once back at the station, Adam simply could not get the scenes from New York out of his head. He finished his shift and returned home where his wife immediately noticed that something was very wrong with him. "I just collapsed at the house. I kept saying 'I just want to die. There are so many mean people out there.' What I did was equate the dead guy in the building with the terrorists hitting the buildings and all the people who died on September 11," said Adam.

"My wife thought I was having a mental breakdown. She took me to the local emergency room. From what I understand, I kept saying 'I don't want to be mean'." Adam was admitted to a local psychiatric hospital, where he was diagnosed with PTSD. Even with all the knowledge he had about traumatic stress and PTSD symptomatology, Adam refused to accept the diagnosis. "I didn't know that I had full blown PTSD. I just thought I was depressed and that my marriage was over. But four days after being admitted to the hospital, I had to go for another interview with another doctor," said Adam, "and the diagnosis was confirmed."

During Adam's stay at the hospital he was very uncomfortable talking about Ground Zero and would avoid speaking about it at all cost. "They would put me into these group therapy sessions, and they would draw it out of me because they wanted me to talk about it," said Adam. "Even then I still didn't want to believe that it was PTSD."

From a physical standpoint, Adam had been plagued by serious lower back pain for the previous year and a half, a steady pain that never seemed to go away. He had sought various forms of medical relief, but nothing had worked. After being admitted to the hospital with PTSD, Adam started participating in individual and group therapy. "The first day that I began talking about New York, I never had the pain again in my back," said Adam.

Adam remained in the hospital for several weeks, where he learned more about PTSD and how it had affected his body, his mind, and his behaviors since returning home from Ground Zero. He began to link his depression and even his extramarital affair with the pain and isolation he felt after experiencing the trauma. "When you're in the middle of PTSD, you don't even know that you have it. I mean, I knew about PTSD. I just didn't connect it with what was happening to me," said Adam.

Search for Support

Adam credits his early recovery with the care he received during his hospitalization. One of the treatment methods that was used with him was a form of "exposure therapy" where, in the controlled treatment environment, his doctors would show him the pictures he took at Ground Zero. "They would have me look at the pictures and then, when a flood of emotions would surface, the doctors would talk me through it," said Adam. "The first time we tried the exposure therapy, I really had an adverse reaction to it. I really lost it for a couple of days." Adam's doctors also helped him identify his "triggers," those things that produced flashbacks for him. Of course one of his biggest triggers had to do with jet planes. Adam's doctors helped him work through the thoughts and feelings that he had associated with the sights and sounds of planes while working at Ground Zero.

During the recovery process, Adam was unsure if he would ever go back to his job. He was not even sure if he wanted to do firefighting anymore. "I didn't want to listen to the sirens any more. I did not want to see the fire trucks anymore, because all of the fire trucks I saw in New York had been crushed. That was another trigger response for me," said Adam. After a few more months of therapy, it was agreed that Adam was ready to return to his job. At that point Adam spoke with the fire department doctor, who was very supportive. "He told me that I had a full career ahead of me. When I heard him say that, my first thought was, 'I still have a job. I still have a career'," said Adam.

Adam's Epilogue

In January of 2004, Adam was cleared to return to full active duty within the fire department and was assigned to a truck company. On an early call, an officer ordered Adam to climb the ladder at a scene. Adam climbed up without any hesitation but, "In the middle of the stick I just froze," said Adam. With assistance from some of his fellow firefighters, Adam was able to come down. After the incident he was temporarily removed from active duty but was not re-hospitalized. He continued his weekly therapy sessions and, after another examination by his doctor, was returned to work in an administrative position, where he remained for nearly three months. At the conclusion of his administrative term, he was returned to full duty, where he works to this day.

Adam reports that in April 2004, his treatment finally came together for him. During a therapy session one day, his doctor explained how a traumatic incident can affect the human mind. "The mind is like a filing cabinet. As we grow up from birth, our minds develop. The mind sees things and files them in different drawers. But when we're exposed to a traumatic incident, something we've never seen before, our mind doesn't know what to do with the image, where to file it, so it stays in place and we can't get past it," recalls Adam of the doctor's explanation. "In the case of New York, there was no filing cabinet drawer for these images. And there were so many images that my mind was overloaded." For Adam, the therapy assisted him in developing a special mental "file cabinet drawer" for the distorted images from New York, permitting him to start to process them, making the images less and less intrusive and upsetting for him.

Once he had the breakthrough in his treatment, Adam began to feel much better about himself and the way that he was able to deal with his PTSD. In the beginning he would avoid any reminders of what he experienced at Ground Zero after September 11. "I now see the triggers for what they are and know that they're not going to kill me. I know that those reminders aren't necessarily going to be comfortable, but I also know that when I encounter them, it's going to be OK," says Adam.

The greatest improvements in Adam's symptom levels and confidence occurred between November 2003 and March 2004. In part, he credits this to the personal and professional support that he received from his department. It would have been easy for Adam's fire department just to retire him and move on, but they did not. The department, and his co-workers, stood along side Adam and supported and encouraged his recovery from PTSD.

The first step that Adam took towards recovery from PTSD was to seek help privately before bringing it to the attention of his department. Looking back over the past couple of years, Adam says that he would recommend therapy to anyone. He admitted, "Having gone through this has made me appreciate all the things I have in my life and the things that I lost. The sad part is that I had to go through something like this to have a better understanding of PTSD and a better understanding of myself."

Chapter Six

Case #3
Chemical Explosion

Monday, October 25, 1993, forever changed the lives of ten firefighters and, indirectly, countless others. For Ben, one of the firefighters involved, the day started as so many other days in the fire station: checking over the protective fire gear, making sure that the equipment was in a ready state, getting a quick briefing of what had happened over the night shift, etc. Ben was detailed to an outlying station for the day, not his normal station or his normal shift mates, because that particular station happened to be short on crew that morning. This was a common practice in Ben's department, as it is for many departments throughout the country.

At around 9:31 a.m., a box alarm was received at the fire alarm dispatch center. Within seconds, the radio silence was broken, and Ben and the rest of his crew were being dispatched to a local chemical company. Ben's engine was the first due company. "When we arrived on scene there was heavy smoke in the area and a report of one explosion," recalled Ben. He began to collect information about the call and formulate a strategy for dealing with the incident, relying on a mixture of incoming information, more than 22 years of fire service experience and training, and his knowledge concerning previous calls to this same facility. Ben knew that the fire department and the chemical company policies called for the employees of the company to assist the fire department in extinguishing sodium fires at the facility, and that was exactly what they were dealing with that morning.

When sodium and water combine, they release a hydrogen gas and cause an explosion. According to Meidi (1970) as this sodium-water reaction takes place, it is typical for dense smoke and a caustic soda to be produced. The caustic soda can cause burns to any exposed skin on the human body, most notably parts with higher levels of moisture such as the mucous membranes and the eyes. The smallest amount of moisture can cause a volatile action. Ben remembered, "We had trained there before. Their employees would hand us salt barrels and tools because you had to use the salt to extinguish the sodium fires."

The chemical company had a long history of safe operations in this process. They had special "burn rooms" where the sodium containers would be moved and the remaining sodium trapped inside the container would be safely burned off. The company had utilized the "burning off" method as a means of reducing the leftover sodium into a harmless ash for a number of years. The method was nothing new to either the fire department or the chemical company. "The burn room was usually used to burn off sodium in a container, much like a 55 gallon drum," said Ben. "The process of burning off the sodium normally involved less than a couple of pounds. This time it looked like about 125 pounds of sodium was burning. It looked like lava." The majority of the sodium was inside the barrel but small amounts of it were also on the floor.

As the fire crew prepared to enter the burn room, none of the chemical company employees told the fire department about the unusually high amount of sodium currently on fire. Ben and the rest of his engine crew crammed into the burn room, which was small and very cramped, especially considering that there were nine firefighters standing in the room and the adjacent hallway, all wearing full protective fire gear and self-contained breathing apparatus.

One of the firefighters had taken a shovel into the burn room with him. The shovel had been put down on the burn room floor for only a couple of seconds as they prepared themselves for their job. Apparently, it was at this point that the shovel must have had contact with moisture from the burn room floor, possibly the drain area. (Little did the firefighters know that this particular burn room was also used as a washroom!) And as the firefighter took a scoop of salt to apply it to the burning sodium, a violent explosion took place.

"I don't know if the barrel tipped over or what happened, but all of a sudden it blows and we all went flying," said Ben. The force of the explosion knocked nine, fully-geared firefighters off their feet and threw them like rag-dolls some distance away. "After the explosion, that's when all hell broke loose. I was thrown about twenty-five feet," said Ben. As they each landed in different locations, their protective fire gear was charred or still burning; their air-packs had been blown off, and in many cases only the metal connectors with melted straps remained where their packs had once been.

When the explosion took place, it produced a dense cloud of sodium oxide fumes coupled with small particles of burning sodium. "It was like a hydrogen bomb going off," said Ben. (It has been reported that sodium can burn in excess of 1600 degrees Fahrenheit.) Just seconds after the explosion, as the firefighters regained some sense of direction, they scrambled down the corridor leading to the outside, each one helping another along the way, patting out their burning gear as they scrambled outside.

"At this point we made it out into the parking lot. I remember Kyle [a fellow firefighter] was standing next to me and his shirt collar was still burning and I was patting it out for him. Even the chief was patting out the firefighters' gear. That's how he got his hands burned," said Ben. "There are other things that happened that very moment that I just don't remember. I still don't know how we could all be standing there, literally touching each other, and we all received different types of burns."

The assistant fire chief received burns to both of his hands from patting out the firefighters' gear as they exited the building. Today the chief still vividly recalls how the firefighters looked "all black and unrecognizable" as they emerged from the building, an image that the chief believes will always be with him.

74

After the Incident

All ten men (nine firefighters and the chief) were burned, and four required hospitalization for their injuries. It was during the long weeks in the hospital that the firefighters began to understand just how long a recovery process this was going to be and just how lucky they had been to survive such an explosion. They would have to endure skin grafts, numerous operations, and the threat of infections. The pain and suffering that each of the men had to endure was indescribable. "Four of us had spent about three weeks in the hospital. The drugs had done their job so we were pretty doped up with all the pain medication," said Ben.

Within days of the explosion, Dr. Thompson, chief psychologist for the Fire Department, arrived in each of the firefighter's rooms. "I remember Jack sticking his head in the room and explaining who he was. I told him, 'I don't need you, get the hell out.' After all, my daughter is a certified social worker and if I needed anything she could help me," said Ben. That first, gruff encounter would end up being the beginning of a significant and steadfast relationship, one that Ben credits with saving his life.

Eventually three of the firefighters would have to endure extremely painful physical therapy each day for about a year. "All the guys from the department would volunteer their time to come and pick up the three of us and bring us to and from physical therapy. They would pick us up at our houses, and if we needed anything at the store, they would drive us," said Ben. Although the chief's physical injuries seemed insignificant compared to those of the other firefighters, he may have emerged with the most significant psychological injuries, eaten up by guilt and feeling ultimately responsible for the injuries to his men. After all, he had been the one to send the men into the building in the first place.

At first, each of the firefighters felt immersed in an ongoing process of continuous and intimate contact with their fellow firefighters, their department, and their community. This was seen as a large social support network for the firefighters. Ben remembers with fondness the sincere concern that he and the other firefighters were shown during that first year of recovery. "There was so much going on at that time. People were bringing meals to us each night. You didn't have time to think about how screwed up you were. Each day you'd ride to physical therapy with a brother firefighter and discuss the daily rumors, policy changes, union happenings, and other fire station chatter. During this time we still felt like we were part of the department," said Ben. "Then, after about a year, they stopped coming over. The department started talking about retiring us on a disability. After all, they needed to get back to their business."

From Trouble to PTSD

From a physical standpoint, Ben had more than enough to deal with. He had trouble walking and decreased hearing in one ear, and he was still recovering from his severe burns. During the first several months, the focus for Ben was on healing from the physical injuries. "Those are the things you think about, rather than the nightmares and the flashbacks," said Ben. "It's when you start feeling better physically and the fire cars aren't there each day that you start to realize there's a lot more work to be done. When there aren't twenty people in your house and stuff like that: basically when you get out on your own." The next few months were, perhaps, the most tenuous ones for Ben as his physical injuries began to heal, yet his psychological injuries had not yet completely surfaced.

Approximately five months post-incident, Ben began to develop some of the physical and emotional symptoms that are commonly experienced by someone who has been through a traumatic incident. "I developed hot and cold flashes and I couldn't sleep a full night. Even today, I wake up every couple of hours," said Ben.

"One of the triggered responses that I have is when I hear sirens. I don't even notice, but other people do. I jump when I hear a siren." An acute psychological change that took place in Ben was that the reality of his mortality had finally sunk in. He could have been killed! This feeling of mortality was in stark contrast to his thoughts and beliefs prior to the incident and challenged his overall sense of safety, security, and control.

The assistant fire chief was later hospitalized because of his psychological injuries. "If the doctors hadn't intervened, I would have committed suicide. I had planned how and when I was going to commit suicide," the chief admits. Today, the chief still struggles with some of the symptoms of PTSD but less frequently and at a much less intense level. During one interview, the chief seemed very thankful for all that the city did for the firefighters injured at this incident. The total environment was considered to be very supportive and the medical care that the chief received not only saved his life but, by his own estimation, made him a stronger person.

Search for Support

It was during that first year that Ben began seeing Dr. Thompson. Ben's willingness to speak with a psychologist was not without a fight, however. He only agreed to talk with Dr. Thompson if his daughter would stop nagging him about seeking out professional help to deal with the incident. Ben was not interested in talking to someone who did not understand the fire service or what he had gone through in the chemical explosion. "People like me don't want to talk with a stuffed shirt," Ben quipped. Dr. Thompson was just the perfect fit for Ben's needs.

When the fire department started the process of retiring the injured firefighters, the social support network began to break down. And as the fire service relationship began to break down, Ben turned to his family, his religion, and other institutions to get basic social support and to add structure to his life. "I had wonderful support at home from my wife and kids. They were by my side each and every day. This helped immensely," said Ben. Over the long painful recovery, Ben's wife was given special training on how to change his bandages. For Ben, a big burly firefighter, it was difficult to rely on his wife for so much. Ben is the first to admit that his grandchildren also tremendously improved his outlook on life.

During one of the interviews with Ben and his family, they revealed that it was several years after the explosion before the wives of the firefighters spoke openly with one another about what happened at the chemical plant that day. It was only after attending a Mass to commemorate the tenth anniversary of the explosion that the wives went out to dinner as a group and, for the first time ever, discussed the impact that the explosion had had on them and their families. It was not their intent to discuss the day of the incident—it just happened! One of the wives commented on what she had been doing when she was notified of the explosion and of her husband's injury. Then another of the wives added what she had been doing. Soon, everyone was sharing her own personal version of the story. Over the course of the next several hours, each wife began to open up about how she felt when she heard the news and what she had done to deal with it over the past ten years. "Yes, individually the wives had talked but not about the incident and never as a group," said Ben's wife. "You couldn't have planned the dinner meeting any better." In the simplest form, the wives had finally, informally debriefed themselves, ten years after the chemical explosion!

Ben's Epilogue

It has been more than ten years since the explosion, and today Ben still experiences some of the symptoms of PTSD. According to Ben, they are not as frequent or as powerful as they have been in the past, but they are still present. Ben still sometimes re-experiences the incident in the form of flashbacks, daydreams, and nightmares. "I can go days without thinking of it," says Ben, "Then some little thing will bring me right back to that point when the explosion occurred, a simple thing, like watching the evening news and hearing about firefighters being caught in an explosion, and it's like I'm right back there."

During the past ten years, Ben has distanced himself from the city and the site of the explosion. He now lives in a small town, located about 40 minutes away from the city. Ben made it very clear that if he were still on the job he would not be living in this rural area. But during Ben's long recovery period, he often came to this rural home, which he had already owned for years by that time, and it became a kind of safe haven for him: a place where he could escape and live his life without the constant reminders of the city and the pain he experienced while working there.

Ben admits that, even ten years later, he only returns to the city twice a year. During the early years, he had to return to the city for doctors' appointments three and four times per week. When in the city, Ben still avoids the location of the explosion at all cost and will go out of his way not to drive by the chemical plant.

Moving away from the city made life easier for Ben in a number of ways: emotionally, mentally, and even physically. His wife still lives and works in the city and comes down to be with him on the weekends. For Ben, it's nice to know that very few of his country neighbors know what he went through. They only know that he is a retired firefighter who misses the job and the cohesiveness of his old department. "As Dr. Thompson has said, 'You never get over it.' I've learned that I'll never get over it. It just gets a little easier. Then there are things, like doing this interview, that can stir things up again for me," said Ben. "Is this easy for me? No way. This [interview] is going to bring down a whole bunch of shit for a while. But I know it could help someone else." Ben made a conscious decision to flood himself with memories of the chemical explosion and the psychological pain that it caused him in order to help others understand what people have to live with when they have PTSD and to let people know that they don't have to go it alone.

Looking back, Ben said that he had a feeling of invincibility as a young firefighter. He admits this was not always a good thing but that it was/is a common feeling among people in the profession. Some firefighters need this feeling in order to do the job. Today, as a retiree, Ben feels much differently: about himself, about life, and about the need for professional help in recovering from psychological trauma. "Even stubborn, dumb as a stump guys like me can see that there's someone to talk with who can talk my language," said Ben.

Chapter Seven

Treating PTSD

With proper early intervention, even someone who has been greatly impacted by a critical incident at work may not develop PTSD. Other people who have been traumatized will find that their symptoms naturally resolve on their own. However, for a variety of reasons, some people will go on to develop PTSD and will need to seek treatment in order to avoid the devastation experienced by the fire personnel discussed in the previous chapters. Good, timely help can make all the difference in recovering from PTSD. But how will you know where to find that help? Or what kind of help you need? Or whether or not it's working? The following chapter will address answers to these questions as we discuss the different types of mental health professionals you may encounter in your search for help and the various techniques they may enlist to relieve you of your symptoms.

Where Can You Turn?

Finding a mental health professional (MHP) can be an overwhelming task. There are numerous varieties of MHPs, some of whom may be approved providers with your insurance carrier, many of whom may not have prior experience in treating PTSD.

The first part of your search for help may involve contacting your insurance carrier in order to get a list of their pre-approved mental health providers. You are likely to see a variety of initials on the list, including M.A., L.C.S.W., Ph.D., Psy. D., and even an M.D. or two. But what do all the different initials mean?

Generally speaking, anyone on your provider's list should be, and is likely to be, a licensed professional. Different professions (and different states) have different educational requirements for licensure. Often, in order to obtain licensure a person must first obtain an advanced degree (beyond the Bachelor's level) and then pass a comprehensive test for their specialization. We recommend that you always ask whether the provider is licensed and by what governing body. Remember that the most effective treatments for PTSD are only available from someone with an advanced degree (Master's level or above), so please check qualifications carefully.

At the Master's level you may encounter good, qualified help from any number of professionals, including someone from a counseling/psychology background (MA, MS, CPC, etc.) or social work background (LCSW-C, LGSW, MSW, etc.). At the doctoral level, you may find social workers (DSW), psychologists (PhD or PsyD), or psychiatrists (MD). Choosing which MHP to go to for help should be a blend of expertise and practicality: you need to find someone who is qualified, who has experience (if not expertise) in PTSD, who is covered by your provider, and who has room in their case load to get you immediate help.

Once all of these qualifications have been met, there is also the question of "fit." Scores of studies on psychotherapy (Bergin & Garfield, 1994) seem to reach the same conclusion: the best therapeutic relationships are those in which the client and the therapist are a good match for one another. If you don't like the therapist when you talk to them or you feel that they're lecturing instead of listening and offering suggestions, then it's probably time to start looking elsewhere for help.

If you either do not have mental health insurance coverage or will not be using it when seeking treatment, you can obtain lists of practitioners in your area by contacting the state licensing board (e.g., Maryland Board of Social Work) or state professional organizations (e.g., Maryland Psychological Association) or by letting your fingers do the walking through the yellow pages. If you personally know someone who works in the mental health field, it can be helpful to ask whom they would recommend or whom they would avoid. Another possible way to find help is to ask for a referral from your primary care physician (although chances are slim that they will know a PTSD expert) or from someone you know who has been treated for PTSD in the past. Some treatments, like EMDR, have a specialized association consisting of practitioners whom they have trained. If you know that you are interested in receiving a certain type of treatment, then you can contact the training organization directly, and they may be able to provide you with a list of competently trained MHPs in your area (see Appendix B for a list of potential referral sources along with their contact information). However you find an MHP, make sure that you check qualifications carefully and that you feel comfortable working with them.

Another characteristic that may send a potential therapist to the top of your list is an understanding of who you are and what your job is all about. The first several sessions with any new therapist will be devoted to taking your personal history. A great amount of time can be saved at the very beginning if the therapist already knows something about the "fire culture," including the language, camaraderie, and stressors that are a normal part of the job. Researchers of psychotherapy have emphasized that the personality of the person being treated is as important to consider as what they are being treated for (Everly & Lating, 2004). A therapist familiar with the rescue personality discussed in Chapter 1 is also likely to understand the enormous sense of control and responsibility that may be contributing to the development of PTSD and be more effective at targeting those beliefs in the course of treatment.

What Can You Expect?

Once you select a qualified therapist who seems to fit with your needs and style, you can begin to grapple with the PTSD symptoms. The course your treatment takes will vary considerably depending on the type of mental health practitioner you select and the type of therapy they practice.

Traditional Treatments for PTSD

As we discussed in Chapter 3, PTSD symptoms fall into three categories: intrusion, avoidance, and arousal. Traditional therapeutic approaches that have shown some success in eliminating these symptoms include Behavior Therapy, Cognitive-Behavioral Therapy, and the use of medications, known as pharmacotherapy.

Behavior Therapy

Behavioral treatments of PTSD often utilize some form of exposure paired with relaxation, such as having the client imagine aspects of the traumatic incident while practicing relaxation. Some of the terms you may hear associated with this form of treatment include "systematic desensitization," "relaxation training," and "biofeedback." Behavioral treatments focus on your physical reactions, such as the increased heart rate and other fear-type responses that occur whenever the traumatic incident is being thought about. In some cases, the client/patient will first be taught to be aware of those physical responses and then taught how to control them. The therapist may have the client think about some aspect of the incident, either gradually increasing the intensity of the image (systematic desensitization) or going straight to the worst part (flooding) and then practice controlling their physical response to it until they find that memories of the trauma no longer produce heightened feelings of anxiety or fear.

Cognitive-Behavioral Therapy

Therapists with a cognitive-behavioral orientation would argue that the problem is not just what the firefighter saw during the traumatic incident that is producing the PTSD but also what it meant to them. A cognitive-behavioral therapist will work with the client to understand the meaning they attached to the traumatic event, challenge errors in facts and beliefs, and also train the client in relaxation/stress-management techniques. The goal is to pair new thoughts and associations with the traumatic incident, thereby making the event feel less upsetting and decreasing the symptoms associated with it. Cognitive-Behavioral Therapy (CBT) takes many of the elements of Behavior Therapy and then goes a step further by adding in cognitions.

Pharmacotherapy

Sometimes a person is so overwhelmed by the symptoms associated with PTSD that conducting psychotherapy is difficult. In addition, people experiencing PTSD often develop other psychological disorders (the issue of "comorbidity" was discussed chapter 3 and will be adrressed again later in this chapter), such as depression and chemical abuse/dependency, which are known to be responsive to drug treatment. In these cases the client may seek help from a psychiatrist (a medical doctor specializing in medications that affect thoughts and behaviors), or other medical provider with prescription privileges.

Because of the variety of biological responses associated with PTSD and the symptom overlap with other disorders, many different classes of psychotropic medications have been used in treatment. Among the drug classes used with PTSD are SSRIs (including Fluoxetine and Sertraline) and related serotonergic agents (including Trazodone and Buspirone), MAOIs (including Phenelzine), TCAs (including Desipramine and Imipramine), Benzodiazepines, Anticonvulsants, and Antispychotics.

Although pharmacotherapy is often suggested as a

part of a PTSD treatment regimen, it is important to remember that it can be expensive, that side effects may occur, and that treatment compliance is mandatory in order to achieve therapeutic results.

InnovativeTreatments for PTSD

Within the past 10 to 15 years some very innovative (and highly effective) therapeutic treatments for PTSD have been developed, researched, and accepted. Among them are Eye Movement Desensitization and Reprocessing (EMDR) and Thought Field Therapy (TFT). Unlike the more traditional treatment approaches, which were developed to treat other disorders and then applied to PTSD, EMDR and TFT were specifically developed to treat traumatized clients.

EMDR

Eye Movement Desensitization and Reprocessing (EMDR) is a multi-component treatment that rests, more or less, on the assumption that when psychological trauma occurs, a person is unable psychologically and biologically to process the event as they would process a normal experience (Chemtob, Tolin, van der Kolk, & Pitman, 2000). The trauma is so "out of the ordinary" that we have no place to file it away in our brains. It is believed that a self-healing process is activated by engaging in rapid eye movements (or other stimulation, such as hand tapping) and that the stimulation makes the person more able to cognitively and physically integrate the trauma. The eye movements, or other physical stimulation, are paired with the thoughts and physical sensations associated with the trauma, given a number on a severity scale (known as a "SUD"), and replaced with an alternative thought or feeling during the course of treatment. For instance, the person receiving treatment may replace the thought "It's all my fault that the patient died" with "I did the best that could be done under the circumstances" or replace a feeling of extreme tension in the neck with a feeling of relaxation.

TFT

Thought Field Therapy (TFT) is based upon the premise that it is not the memory associated with a trauma that is the problem but rather the severe emotional pain associated with the memory of the trauma. The originator of TFT, Roger Callahan, describes it as a mixture of biology, clinical psychology, applied kinesiology (chiropractic), acupuncture, and quantum physics (Callahan & Callahan, 2000). In TFT the patient is asked to think about the upsetting event, quantify it on a scale from 1 to 10 (10 being the most upsetting), and follow with tapping on the body in specific places (energy points) in a specific pattern. The treatment is very brief and has been reported to produce nearly immediate relief. Rather than having the memories of the trauma erased, a person may actually report that following treatement the image or memory of the event is even clearer than before treatment but that it no longer carries the intense emotional response that it once did.

More is Better

Just as a tool kit containing several good tools is better than a tool kit with just a wrench, a therapist who knows how to treat PTSD with numerous approaches or techniques is likely to be more effective than a therapist who is limited to just a single therapeutic approach. That way, if you don't seem to be responding to one type of treatment you can try something else without having to change therapists and start the process all over again. Usually therapists who have been trained in EMDR or TFT also have training in some form of Behavioral or Cognitive-Behavioral Therapy. And if you are lucky enough to find one of these MHPs who is also covered by your insurance and who understands fire personnel, you've hit the equivalent of a PTSD trifecta.

How Do You Know It's Working?

In some ways a psychological trauma is very similar to a physical trauma. In both cases it takes time for the injury to heal, and in both cases there may be scars or reminders of what was experienced. Treatments such as TFT and EMDR are considered short-term (3 months or less) and may even show improvement after the first few sessions. Pharmacotherapy may take a month or more (depending on the medication) before the drugs reach a therapeutic level in a person's system and symptom reductions are experienced.

89

Complications

For many people there may be other factors complicating the therapeutic progression, making the road to healing feel as if it's filled with stop signs and potholes. One complication that can affect the course of recovery is the presence of anniversaries. The six-month or one-year anniversary of the trauma may trigger a re-emergence of symptoms: symptoms that may have felt like they were under control. Be patient with yourself or your loved one around anniversaries. Another complicating factor is the presence of other psychological problems or "comorbidity." PTSD alone can be very difficult to treat, but if the trauma was years in the past and has spawned secondary problems such as depression or substance abuse, it can be even more challenging. Some therapists choose to address one issue at a time, such as getting a client off drugs before tackling the trauma issue. Others may attack the various problems all at once with a variety of methods, such as an antidepressant for the depression, substance abuse counseling for the addiction, and cognitive-behavioral therapy for the trauma. Make sure that your treatment provider is aware of any secondary problems that you may be dealing with, even PTSD is the primary reason you are seeking treatment.

Treatment Compliance

Even the best treatments won't work if you don't stick with them. Treatment compliance can be difficult for people working through their trauma because of the need to confront their pain, even though the short-term intensity may actually signal the beginning of healing. Sometimes people stop taking medications because they no longer feel anxious or depressed, failing to consider the fact that it is the medicine that is contributing to their improvement. We would advise people to always consult their treatment provider before discontinuing medication or therapy so that the reasons for stopping are adequately explored and, if necessary, alternative treatment arrangements can be made.

A final note on compliance concerns the hazards of sharing medications. Despite knowing the dangers of taking someone else's medications, well-meaning friends or family members may offer to give a person with PTSD their Xanax or Valium because they see that the person is suffering and because they are unsure how else to help. Prescription medications should never be taken by anyone other than the prescribed patient. You can take their advice, you can take their support, but don't ever take their medications!

In Summary

Treating PTSD requires several steps and decisions. First, a person must find a mental health professional (MHP), either through their insurance carrier, by referrals from physicians or friends, or through inquiries to professional organizations, state licensing boards, etc. Competent care can be provided by a variety of MHPs, but it is helpful if the provider is familiar with the fire service and possesses some experience or expertise with PTSD. It is also very important that the person seeking treatment feel comfortable with the MHP whom they choose. A variety of therapeutic treatments can be used for PTSD. Some of the more traditional treatments include Behavior Therapy, Cognitive-Behavioral Therapy, and pharmacotherapy. More innovative trauma treatments include EMDR and TFT. Once an MHP has been selected and treatment has begun, it is important to remember that recovery is often filled with setbacks (especially around anniversaries); that it sometimes hurts more before it begins to feel better; that the presence of other disorders, such as depression or substance abuse, can complicate and prolong treatment; and that in order for treatment to be effective you need to stick with it.

Chapter Eight

Preparing and Protecting Your Own

Some have attempted to argue that the present system for dealing with traumatic stress in the fire service is not broken, that most firefighters are tough enough to handle even the worst incident thrown at them (just give them a couple of beers and they'll be good as new), and that only the weak become traumatized. This smacks of a "blame-the-victim" mentality and fails to adequately take into consideration the situational factors that impinge upon a firefighter during and after an incident. Yes, most firefighters do remarkably well handling things that would overwhelm the average person. But when a firefighter does become traumatized, we have to remember that their response is normal, not abnormal.

Exposure to an event involving physical injury or threat to oneself or another person is part of the diagnostic criteria for ASD and PTSD. Given the amount of exposure that firefighters have to these types of events throughout their careers, perhaps the most amazing thing is that more firefighters do not develop PTSD. Apparently some things must be working well. However, when you consider the fact that a firefighter is more than twice as likely as someone in the general population to develop PTSD and that every time a firefighter is forced to retire early from the fire service or goes out on disability it costs upwards of $75,000 to train and equip their replacement (a significant amount of money for even a wealthy department), it is obvious that more remains to be done.

The three stories presented in this book represent what can happen when a firefighter has a call that sticks with them and either fails to recognize that he is in need of professional help or refuses to take help when offered. Common sense tells us that if the men in the case stories had received crisis intervention assistance immediately after their bad incident, the effect that it had on their lives could have been minimized. Early intervention is a critical component in identifying people at risk for PTSD and essential in mitigating the impact that it has on a person's life. But early intervention is just one part of a larger, system-wide change that needs to take place in order to increase awareness of, and services for, traumatized firefighters.

The purpose of the following chapter is not to present the reader with an overview of the research underlying the field of crisis intervention, but rather, to describe the variety of crisis intervention services that can be provided to fire personnel and the way in which they can fit together to form a comprehensive system. Anyone wishing to know more about research with firefighters is encouraged to read some of the more recent literature in the field, including "Crisis Intervention: A Review" (Flannery and Everly, 2000) and/or "The Debriefing 'Controversy' and Crisis Intervention: A Review of Lexical and Substantive Issues" (Everly & Mitchell, 2000).

Numerous steps can be taken before and after a call (some simple, some more complex) as part of a comprehensive program for the prevention and mitigation of psychological trauma. The following chapter will address these issues according to when services should be provided and for whom:

Early Preparation
- Changing the fire culture
- Increasing education and awareness
- Including families
- Using a systematic approach

Early Intervention
- Formal and informal support services
- Crisis intervention services
- The importance of follow-up

Treatment
- Who can refer
- When to refer
- Where to refer

Early Preparation
(a.k.a. "pre-planning")

Changing the Fire Culture

In chapter 1 we addressed the firefighter personality and the way it is influenced by the larger fire culture. Any attempt to decrease the rates of PTSD in firefighters must begin with changing the traditional fire culture and its view of psychological trauma: i.e., from one of blame and judgment that trauma is weakness and abnormality to one of compassion and understanding. In order for these views to change, people must first acknowledge that a problem exists. As they say in the world of addictions, admitting that you have a problem is the first step.

A fire culture burdened with the idea that only "the

weak ones" get hurt is also a culture that discourages a firefighter from seeking help. It is one that claims to be rooted in resiliency while its own weakness limits its potential for growth. Instead of enhancing a firefighter's natural strengths by adopting a prevention approach or assisting in recovery through early intervention, this perspective almost dooms the traumatized firefighter and makes their recovery much more difficult than it needs to be. It reinforces the idea of personal blame and, by doing so, absolves itself from responsibility.

In chapter 3 we mentioned the need for more research concerning the incidence and prevalence of ASD and PTSD in firefighters. It is easy for the fire service, as a whole, to dismiss the idea of psychological trauma as long as it is permitted to gloss over the issue as an occasional occurrence. If we really knew how many firefighters going out on early retirement, physical disabilities, or for other "personal" reasons actually had a traumatic incident pushing them out of their careers, it would be much more difficult to deny. Better, more accurate numbers concerning just how many firefighters were negatively affected by traumatic stress and how much of a burden it was placing on their departments could be an impetus for bringing the issue out from the shadows of the fire culture.

Remember back in chapter 1 when we talked about the fire service being like links of a chain, with everyone working together to achieve the best possible outcome (one of the genuine strengths of the fire culture)? This same mentality should be invoked when dealing with traumatic stress. As long as one firefighter is hurting, the chain is weakened. By helping a fellow firefighter you are not only helping a colleague in need, you are improving the functioning of your whole organization—and possibly even learning something yourself!

Education and Awareness

Education is at the foundation of almost every prevention program or pre-planning mission. Any firefighter will tell you that educating the public about fire hazards in the home and in the workplace is an integral, prevention-oriented part of their job. Knowing ahead of time how many entrance or exit points there are in a building will save valuable time when the structure is ablaze. Likewise, in order to prevent or mitigate traumatic stress reactions, people must first understand psychological trauma and its symptoms and be aware of the kinds of situations that are most likely to cause a negative reaction. Educating firefighters about traumatic stress can begin in the fire academy. A segment on traumatic stress could easily be woven into the coursework that every new firefighter receives, along with other essential education concerning equipment and procedures. While most departments probably already cover a segment on how the victims they treat may react to their own trauma, many probably do not address the issue from the rescuers' point of view. (Neglecting the topic of vicarious traumatization may contribute to a misunderstanding of why they have been impacted and make the firefighter feel like a victim himself.)

97

Conducting this type of education in the fire academy setting can achieve two positive results with very little effort on the part of the fire service. First, it prepares the new firefighters for the psychological hazards of the job so that if—or when—they have a bad call, they understand that what they are experiencing is a normal reaction and they know that services are in place to help them recover as quickly as possible from the trauma. Secondly, it creates a culture of understanding and support, showing the firefighter that their new profession is concerned not just about their physical safety but also about their psychological well-being.

Starting with education in the fire academy is just that: a start. Just like the continuing education that firefighters receive in other aspects of their skills and knowledge, continuing education concerning traumatic stress is essential. Traumatic stress, ASD and PTSD, and the secondary disorders that often accompany these diagnoses (i.e., the issues of Substance Abuse and Depression that were covered in chapter 3) can all be part of the continuing education curriculum. The information should be provided to all personnel, up and down the line and across the ranks.

This type of information also needs to be shared with the families of the firefighters, starting in the academy and continuing throughout the firefighters' careers. Educating family members can be done in a variety of ways: information can be mailed home, courses can be provided just for the families, and some information sessions can include the firefighters along with their family members. By providing some structured opportunities for firefighters and their families to learn about psychological trauma together, a department ensures that all parties involved are working with the same information, and it opens the flow of communication on what may be a difficult topic for some to address.

Families

Family members are a critical component of the system for a number of reasons, and as such, deserve the same information and support that we give our firefighters. First, family members often see the firefighter in unstructured situations, which may allow them a better glimpse into just how the firefighter has been affected by an incident. At home the firefighter's increase in irritability, sleep disturbance, or alcohol consumption may be more prominent than at work (where such behaviors have the potential to jeopardize one's job). For this reason, a family member who is knowledgeable about ASD and PTSD can be an important resource for identifying when a firefighter has been traumatized.

In addition, family members are likely to be indirectly impacted by the trauma when the firefighter brings these symptoms home. According to Simpson and Simpson (1997), PTSD has a tremendous impact on relationships. Increased irritability may produce outbursts of anger directed at family members, and the feelings of anxiety and depression can severely strain a relationship, especially if the family member is not aware of the source of the behavior change. Since these behavioral changes may result from a variety of causes, not just a work-related trauma, the family members need to have a pre-established open line of communication with the firefighter so that they feel comfortable asking about and discussing a bad call with their loved one when it occurs. This type of communication needs to be established prior to a critical incident, not when a firefighter is trying to avoid reminders of a bad call. Prior knowledge concerning ASD and PTSD will help the family members understand where the new anger or irritability is coming from and can relieve some of the pressure when stress levels are high and coping skills are rapidly being depleted.

Family members may also find that they have their own feelings to deal with when their loved one has been psychologically injured at work. They may feel outraged that the injury occurred, especially if they believe that someone else was to blame. They may feel disgusted or betrayed if they think their loved one was treated unfairly either during or after the injury. They may experience grief over the changes that have occurred as the result of the psychological trauma (Flannery, 2004). In other words, family members need to be included in prevention, education, and crisis intervention services for their own sake, as well as for the sake of the firefighter.

A Systematic Approach

If you want to catch a fish, it may be easier to use a net than just a single hook, and "catching" someone who is experiencing a posttraumatic stress response can be thought of in much the same way. The more people who know what types of reactions to look for, the more likely it is that a traumatized person will be identified before it is too late. For this reason we recommend a multi-component approach to dealing with traumatic stress in the fire service. If your fellow firefighters don't spot the problem, then maybe your spouse will. If the education you received about traumatic stress doesn't make it any easier to deal with a bad call, then maybe the crisis intervention services will. If the chaos and unpredictability of the traumatic incident overwhelm you, then maybe knowing that a comprehensive system is in place can help restore a sense of control and balance to your life.

When we say "systematic" we are referring to a pre-established set of services designed to assist a firefighter before and after exposure to a traumatic incident. Establishing this system and providing services prior to being needed (e.g., providing education on ASD and PTSD while firefighters are still in the academy setting) can normalize the issue, reassure the firefighter, and ensure that the response is well thought out, rather than a hasty decision made when people are upset and services may not be available. A comprehensive, systematic plan also ensures that the system has a back-up (and possibly that the back-up has a back-up) and that provisions are made for a variety of contingencies. This type of psychological preparedness fits nicely with the meticulous, control-oriented aspects of the firefighter personality discussed in chapter 1—and besides those firefighters always like to have a plan.

Early Intervention

Formal and Informal Sources of Support

Peers

Friendship, team-work, and shared experiences make fellow firefighters the most likely, and probably the most common, source of support after a bad call. Informal discussions naturally occur in many instances: in the bunk room as firefighters are trying to unwind after a late night call out, in the kitchen the next morning, in the break room as the next shift comes on duty and the details of the events are relayed. Sometimes the discussions are more procedural in nature, with an informal critique woven throughout. Other times they are merely a recounting of what each person saw or experienced during the critical incident. The shared experiences increase the likelihood that another firefighter will understand what you saw or experienced. The shared reactions can help normalize the outcome. The different perspectives offered by others on the scene may help shed light on what an individual firefighter didn't see while the incident was occurring. All of these aspects can be incredibly helpful, if and when they occur on their own. This is one of the pre-existing aspects of the fire service that works well when it is properly utilized.

In some instances, however, a firefighter who is seriously impacted by a call will avoid talking about it (remember the avoidance symptoms we discussed in chapter 3?) and the natural, informal support will not be sought out. When this occurs, a trained peer support person can help tremendously. These trained "peers" are fire personnel (not mental health professionals) who have received specialized training in psychological trauma and crisis intervention techniques. They are trained to recognize a bad call that might require outside assistance for all personnel involved. Peers are also trained to recognize when a fellow firefighter may be having trouble dealing with a call and how to assess their level of distress. They should have immediate access to referral information when necessary. A trained peer is more likely to seek out someone in distress, whereas many firefighters might

feel that they are being intrusive if they seek out someone who is isolating themselves after a bad call.

The benefits of using trained peers are numerous.
Since they are part of the fire crew, a trained peer is
more likely to spot an incident or individual requiring assistance, and they can do so much earlier than someone who is not regularly at the station. Trained peers
have the same experiences as other firefighters, but
their specialized training may make them more effective
at providing support to those most in need and may
help them do so in a more effective manner. Another
substantial benefit to using peers for more formal crisis
intervention services is that they do not tend to carry
the same stigma as an EAP or other mental health professional. A firefighter may be reluctant to talk about
their reaction to a traumatic incident with an EAP for fear
that others in their department will find out that they are
receiving formal mental health services. For some people,
talking to a mental health professional is the equivalent
of admitting that you are "crazy." When you talk to a
trained peer, no one needs to know whether you are
discussing your reaction to a bad incident or a bet on a
baseball game. And since the other firefighters interact
with trained peers on a daily basis as they fulfill their
normal roles as firefighters, their presence is considered
normal and natural, unlike the inclusion of a mental health
professional whose presence may signal that something
is wrong.

Family

As we mentioned earlier in this chapter, a family member who is educated about trauma and its symptoms

can be an excellent source of support and can also help spot a firefighter in need of more formal assistance. This was the case in two of our case stories. Mike's girlfriend, Sarah, felt helpless at first as she watched his personality change and his career fall apart. Once Mike was diagnosed with PTSD and Sarah was able to view his changes through the lens of psychological trauma, she was better able to support him, encourage him in his treatment, and keep the lines of communication open. For Ben, his daughter's understanding of PTSD was what spurred him on to seek treatment and increased his openness to the therapeutic process.

On the other hand, a family member who does not understand trauma may find that the changes in the relationship are too much to take, as was the case in our second case story. The strains in Adam's marriage finally became too much for his wife, and rather than having his spouse as a source of support, Adam found he was dealing with an additional loss when his marriage ended in divorce.

Family members of traumatized firefighters need support, too. In Adam's case, support for his spouse immediately after he returned from Ground Zero might have helped prepare her for the severity of Adam's reaction and for her own reactions as well. In our first case story, Mike's girlfriend experienced significant personal emotional turmoil as the result of his PTSD. In our third case story, Ben's wife, and the wives of the other injured firefighters, waited 10 years before finally coming together to discuss their own reactions to the incident and the effects it had on their families! Who knows how much easier the whole process could have been for the families of these firefighters if support had been offered immediately after the incidents—support for the traumatized and support for their loved ones. A department that provides good, rapid care for firefighters traumatized on the job may incur less anger and resentment from the personnel's family members than a department that does nothing. And a department that provides care for the family members, themselves, in the form of education, peer support, and referrals (when necessary), will help the family to function effectively following the incident and decrease the over-all level of disruption to the family system.

Chaplains

Fire chaplains are asked to wear several hats in their service to fire departments: comforting victims and their families, assisting with death notifications, performing ceremonial duties, and providing practical as well as spiritual assistance. Their primary role, however, is to provide support to the victims and to the firefighters themselves. In the wake of a traumatic incident, many people may seek out a chaplain or other spiritual leader, hoping to find comfort and guidance in the form of religion or spirituality. Some firefighters find themselves comforted by their belief in God, whereas others feel alienated, asking how God could let something so terrible happen to them or to someone else (Dietz, 2001). While there is certainly an important role for pastoral counseling in the healing process, that role usually comes in the weeks and months following the traumatic incident. In the days and hours that follow a trauma, a chaplain is in a unique position to provide crisis interventions services with the

105

same goals as other types of crisis intervention but with a faith-based twist.

Pastoral crisis intervention can help stabilize and mitigate symptoms of distress and speed emotional recovery through such things as prayer, confessions to ventilate emotions, and the performing of various rituals and sacraments (Everly, 2000). Pastoral crisis intervention is most appropriate when the person is open to and interested in receiving a faith-based perspective to the trauma. It is a vehicle for easing the pain of those who have been traumatized, not for engaging in debates of spiritual or theological issues.

Depending on the department, and the firefighters who work there, a chaplain may be a common sight around the station. As is the case with peers trained in crisis intervention, chaplains may be more likely to be approached by fire personnel and their families for performing pastoral crisis care when the chaplains are known and the personnel and their families are comfortable with them. In order to perform pastoral crisis intervention, clergy members or spiritual leaders do not need to be associated with a fire department, but they do need to receive specialized training in crisis intervention so that they do not mistake its goals and procedures with those of counseling.

EAPs

An Employee Assistance Program (EAP) can provide a variety of services for fire personnel across all levels of intervention for traumatic stress, from prevention to crisis intervention to short-term treatment. A department's EAP could be tapped to provide continuing education on the mental health issues discussed earlier in this chapter or even to assist with the delivery of crisis intervention services. And an internal, departmental EAP may be more familiar with firefighters than an outside agency that provides services for different types of businesses or agencies. Most EAPs offer some type of short-term counseling, but keep in mind that having an EAP associated with a fire department does not ensure that the health care providers are specialized in treating traumatic stress.

EAPs have traditionally been used for issues of substance abuse, depression, or anger management (disorders that can also appear in conjunction with PTSD), but services will vary. The types of services provided will depend upon the size (and wealth) of your department and the size (and expertise) of the EAP. But no matter what the size, confidentiality should always be ensured when services are provided. A firefighter who uses their EAP to relieve symptoms of anxiety or depression needs to feel confident that the information gleaned from treatment will not find its way back to their department in any manner. Treatment records are guaranteed confidentiality, just as are other medical records, and even if a firefighter was referred by their chief to receive treatment from the EAP, their records cannot be released back to the department or any specific treatment information divulged without the patient's permission.

Crisis Intervention Services

Any and all of the early preparation and intervention services we just talked about can be put together in a variety of ways to form a more comprehensive system, but the system used most often for dealing with traumatic stress in the fire service and other emergency service professions is known as Critical Incident Stress Management (CISM; Everly & Mitchell, 1999). CISM is a comprehensive system integrating pre-incident education and a variety of crisis intervention techniques in individual and group formats (Mitchell, 2004). It utilizes a team approach with trained peers, chaplains, and mental health professionals, and the team's members work together to educate, support, and refer firefighters for treatment when necessary.

Pre-crisis preparation is, by definition, preventative in scope and functions to educate, set expectations, and provide stress management skills. Demobilizations (used with large groups only in large scale incidents or disaster), Defusings and Critical Incident Stress Debriefings (used with small groups) are specialized crisis intervention techniques that are provided relatively soon after a traumatic incident and are designed to aid in stress management and the mitigation of symptoms. Individual crisis intervention services (known as "one-to-ones") are the most common services provided by CISM team members and can occur at any time, pre- or post-incident. Pastoral crisis intervention and Family CISM (as described earlier in this chapter) can also occur at any time and may be prompted by a recent event or the emergence of symptoms. CISM also stresses the need for follow-up to occur in conjunction with the other crisis intervention services.

Follow-up

Follow-up to any and all crisis intervention services is critical. Remember in chapter 4 when we mentioned that some traumatic stress reactions have a delayed onset (meaning that the symptoms do not show up for a month or more following exposure to the trauma)? If crisis intervention services are only provided shortly after the trauma, then these people may be missed. In addition, symptoms can worsen over time and a person with mild symptoms after the incident may have higher symptom levels two weeks later. There is also the issue of ASD becoming PTSD.

Another important reason for follow-up is to ensure that people have made phone calls or booked appointments if referrals were given early on. Perhaps they lost the phone number for the therapist, or they forgot to call or decided not to call in the hopes that the symptoms would naturally resolve on their own. With the unpredictable nature of the fire service it may even be that people were handling the first incident reasonably well but were then hit with another difficult call and the cumulative impact was enough to require additional assistance. Whatever the reason, crisis intervention without follow-up is incomplete – and we all know how much firefighters like to see a job through to the end.

Treatment

Issues concerning the treatment of PTSD were covered in chapter 7, but the role of treatment within the larger context of a comprehensive traumatic stress management program is worth mentioning here.

Who Can Refer

A comprehensive traumatic stress management program in the fire service includes a variety of people who may refer an individual for treatment. It may be the firefighter's boss, noticing a diminishing quality of work, who refers the firefighter to an EAP or recommends another source for treatment. It may be a peer (a formally trained peer or another concerned co-worker) or a chaplain who recommends treatment. Family members privy to more global information regarding the severity of the impact of the trauma may be the ones who recommend. And last, but not least, the firefighter may decide on their own that the symptoms are intolerable and either ask another person for a referral or search out services on their own. The beauty of having a comprehensive system lies (at least to some degree) in its redundancy of services and the decreased potential of having a person in need fall through the organizational cracks.

When to Refer

In many instances the key to treatment effectiveness is the same as the idea underlying crisis intervention: the earlier you get to them, the better the prognosis. When a person is in obvious psychological pain, why wait until the problem is chronic and intractable? It is better to refer someone with ASD than to wait until they develop PTSD. And it is better to refer someone with PTSD than to wait until they develop a substance abuse problem in their attempts to self-medicate. And it is always better to refer someone to treatment for depression than to wait until they become suicidal. Do not wait until it is too late.

Where to Refer

A good CISM Team will have a list of mental health professionals (possibly including the ones on the team) who can treat a traumatized firefighter. As we mentioned in chapter 7, if you go through your insurance provider or EAP you may not have a choice in which mental health professional (MHP) you end up with, but it is likely to be less expensive than paying out-of-pocket. Obtaining the services of a mental health professional who understands the fire culture, who is well trained in treating traumatic stress, and who has room in their case load for a new client may be difficult to come by. The most important thing is that you feel comfortable working with your MHP and that you get help before things become worse.

In Summary

A variety of crisis intervention services can be utilized to prepare and protect firefighters from the effects of traumatic stress. Before a traumatic event has even occurred the fire culture can be changed to be more understanding of traumatized firefighters; new recruits and their families can be educated about the signs, symptoms and strategies for treating traumatic stress responses and other disorders; continuing education concerning these topics can occur at all levels of the fire service; and an open dialogue between firefighters and their families can be established concerning ASD and PTSD. A systematic approach to targeting traumatic stress is recommended. Sources of support that can be utilized either individually or as part of a larger crisis intervention support team include peers (informal as well as those formally trained in crisis intervention), family members, chaplains, and EAPs. Anyone providing crisis intervention support services must remember the importance of follow-up to check on those not previously showing signs of distress and to verify that recommendations or referrals were properly utilized. Following a traumatic incident that develops into ASD or PTSD, anyone can refer a firefighter for formal clinical care. It is best to catch a person in need of treatment as early as possible and to have a list of possible providers and/or treatment options available when referrals are made.

Chapter Nine

Summary and Conclusions

Connecting the Dots:
Firefighters and PTSD

While anyone has the potential to be psychologically traumatized at some point in their lives, firefighters constitute a special subpopulation due to their repeated exposure to violent, grotesque, and dangerous stimuli. Many firefighters may complete their careers and experience only mild or brief traumatic stress reactions following a bad call. Others will find that those bad calls stick with them and that the symptoms become more intrusive and problematic over time, leading to disruption in all facets of their lives.

Unfortunately it seems that the things that help a firefighter do their job (and do it well) can be the same things that make it difficult for them to let go of a difficult call, such as having a perfectionistic approach to work, a need for mission completion, and a willingness to accept responsibility and take control. These same aspects of personality are often reinforced within the work setting. A firefighter's meticulous nature is nurtured by repetitive drills. Their sense of responsibility is heightened by working as part of a close team and not wanting to let anyone down. Letting go of a sense of responsibility or accepting the fact that everything was done correctly but that the outcome was still negative can be one of the most challenging aspects of the job.

113

Case Stories: Lessons Learned

The three firefighters whose stories were presented in this book illustrate some very important lessons that we hope you will take with you. The first lesson concerns the fact that even the helpers are not immune to psychological trauma. Somehow we often carry with us the assumption that it is the people who are helped who should be traumatized, not the rescuers. But it is the very nature of helping, being in close proximity to someone seriously injured and employing everything that we know to ease their pain or save their lives, which puts a firefighter at risk as well. And sometimes it is the firefighter who cares the most and works the hardest who will be impacted by the experience to the greatest degree.

Another important point illustrated by the case stories concerns the level of exposure to trauma: you can develop PTSD by being the person in the life-threatening situation, by witnessing another person in that situation, or by hearing about another person in that situation. In the chemical explosion story Ben was physically injured in the incident—a fact that increased his chances of developing PTSD because his own life was threatened in the incident and his physical recovery was lengthy and extremely painful. He became both a helper and the one in need of help as the incident progressed.

The fire chief in the chemical explosion, while experiencing burns to his hands from trying to pat out the burning firefighters as they exited the building, was most affected by his sense of responsibility and guilt for having sent the crew into the building in the first place. It was not his direct trauma, but the experience of witnessing the life-threatening incident of others, that most impacted him. Mike, the fire inspector in our first case story, directly witnessed the body of the deceased woman but he was not physically in jeopardy at any time. Instead, it was the emotional reaction he experienced by looking into the dead woman's face that stuck with him. Both Mike and the fire chief were traumatized by witnessing another person's death or serious injury and identifying with them in some important way. Their own physical safety was never really in jeopardy, but that did not lessen the psychological impact that it had on them at the time, nor did it lessen the impact that it had on their lives in the months and years that followed.

In our case story involving the New York World Trade Center immediately after September 11, Adam was sent to the scene not to help with the rescue and recovery operation but to help the helpers by providing psychological support services to the crews on scene. While he was obviously surrounded by death and destruction for the weeks that he worked there, the most difficult aspect of Adam's job was the vicarious traumatization he experienced by hearing other people's stories of trauma and loss. He found that he was constantly surrounded by people telling their stories, both at work and when he returned to his hotel in his "downtime." Although it may have been cathartic for the person describing the incident, the act of listening to other people's grizzly stories over and over for weeks at a time eventually became a traumatizing experience for Adam. (This is a very important point to remember for anyone working in a psychological support capacity—don't forget your own!)

Another point illustrated in the case stories is the need to make families aware of traumatic stress and the impact that it can have on the firefighters and on themselves. Mike's girlfriend, Sarah, and Ben's family members all saw immediate and drastic changes in their loved one following the traumatic incident. Ben was especially fortunate in that his daughter was in a position to recognize and recommend professional assistance for his PTSD. Sarah was at somewhat of a disadvantage in that she knew something was very wrong with Mike but did not have enough information to realize that the problem had developed into PTSD and had spawned secondary issues, such as a dependence on alcohol.

In all three case stories the family members of the firefighters were also impacted by the traumatic event. Ben's wife faced the potential loss of her husband in the chemical explosion and then had to watch his painful recovery from the burns. Sarah became angered and upset by the way she felt the department treated Mike after his psychological injury. Adam's wife became so confused and discouraged by the changes in his behavior and in their relationship following the trauma that the marriage ended in divorce. Clearly all of these women, and other family members as well (especially parents and children), could have benefited from psychological assistance had it been provided following the firefighters' traumatic incidents.

The case stories also highlight some important ideas concerning the role that a fire department plays when a firefighter has been traumatized. First and foremost, the firefighters must be assured that the department is behind them and will support them in their recovery. The tangible and intangible assistance provided to Ben following the explosion helped to make him feel as if he and his family were still part of the department. The understanding that Adam's fire administration demonstrated by transitioning him into less stressful, temporary positions within the department probably enhanced his recovery while enabling him to continue in his career. He had already lost his marriage. At least he didn't need to worry about losing his career, too.

The pain of the trauma can be compounded when a firefighter feels that his department questions the validity of his psychological reaction. Mike's recovery from PTSD was impeded by his belief that others felt he was malingering, and his avoidance reaction was heightened because he felt ostracized by his peers. One of Mike's key sources of support was lost at a critical point in his life, and instead of being able to turn to his fellow firefighters for support, he withdrew even further from the fire service and everyone associated with it. The chances of this type of adversarial relationship developing should be significantly reduced if a department and firefighter have an open dialogue concerning traumatic stress either before or immediately after an exposure to trauma.

It is important for a department to know their members well so that they can recognize when a firefighter is in trouble. Mike's chief could see that he was upset by what he had experienced at the car fire scene and offered to find him some professional assistance. This was exactly the right thing for a good leader (and a good friend) to do. The key aspect of the situation that was missing was a lack of follow-up. Maybe Mike was reluctant to see a mental health professional at that early point, but he might have been willing to talk to a trained peer, or he might have been more receptive to the idea a few days later. A good administrator will know their personnel, offer assistance when appropriate, and always follow-up, whether or not the assistance was taken.

While Mike and Ben continue to struggle with their symptoms, Adam's story shows us that people can and do recover from PTSD if they receive appropriate treatment, even if that help does not come in the most timely manner. If you or your loved one have PTSD, do not give up hope. Being diagnosed with PTSD does not necessarily mean that your career is over, but it may have to be on hold for a while as the psychological wounds heal. Recovery from psychological trauma is often slow, but it can also be a process filled with personal growth: feeling invincible makes a firefighter do their job without hesitation whereas understanding the fragility of life makes them appreciate the help that they provide even more.

Lessons Learned

- Even the helpers can develop PTSD

- Firefighters can be traumatized through varying levels of exposure:
  - personal life-threatening event
  - exposure to someone else's life-threatening event
  - hearing about another person's life-threatening event

- Family members are impacted, too

- The fire department's actions can affect the impact that the trauma has on the firefighter

- Firefighters can recover from PTSD

Points in Time:
When and How to Intervene

The best system for preventing and mitigating psychological trauma is one that is comprehensive in scope and involves all the stakeholders (i.e., firefighters, family members, and administrators). Remember that the time to plan a response for dealing with traumatic stress in the fire service is not after the trauma has occurred, when people are upset and resources may not be available, but rather, before the trauma, when timing is not critical and back-up contingency plans can be made. This helps ensure that important details are not forgotten at a critical point.

Fire departments need to take the same approach to traumatic stress that they take to preventing fires: education and enforcement. Before the trauma has occurred, fire administrators, firefighters, and their families need to be educated about traumatic stress and how it can affect them. In addition, continuing education should be provided to increase awareness and provide opportunities for the various stakeholders to voice concerns or start a dialogue on the issue. This will help administrators better understand their firefighters and help firefighters and their family members normalize discussions of the trauma experienced at work. Underlying this process is the idea that if theses groups can talk about psychological trauma *before* it has occurred, they will be more likely to acknowledge it and work together to resolve psychological trauma *after* it has occurred.

In the hours, days, and weeks following a difficult call, there are a variety of crisis intervention services that can be provided, such as defusings, debriefings,

119

one-to-one support services, pastoral crisis intervention, family support, etc. Personnel should be screened to determine who may be in need of additional clinical assistance, and referrals should be made, when appropriate. Follow-up is important to ensure that symptom levels have not changed for the worse, that people made use of the referrals given to them, that secondary problems have not developed, and that more assistance is not needed. The whole point of having a crisis intervention system is to use it appropriately, so be careful not to over-utilize or under-utilize your system, or it may lose its effectiveness.

If a firefighter develops Acute Stress Disorder (ASD) or Posttraumatic Stress Disorder (PTSD), therapeutic assistance can be provided by a variety of health professionals and can come in a variety of packages. Pharmacotherapy (the use of medications) can help reduce symptoms of depression or anxiety and increase a person's receptivity to psychotherapy. Psychotherapy can be short-term or long-term in duration and can include any number of traditional approaches (such as Cognitive Behavioral Therapy) or innovative treatments (such as EMDR). The most important things to remember are that you need to feel comfortable with your treatment provider and that you need to follow-through with treatment and not give up if symptoms do not resolve as quickly as you had hoped. Do not quit, do not self-medicate with alcohol or other drugs, and do not isolate yourself from the people who want to help you.

When a firefighter develops ASD or PTSD, a department that understands and is flexible will go a long way towards helping the recovery process. If a firefighter's work status needs to be changed to a temporary disability or light duty, make sure that they know their job will be waiting for them when they are ready to return. If a firefighter has to take time away to receive treatment, make sure that they know they are still part of the organization by keeping them up-to-date on activities in the department. Don't give up on the traumatized firefighter—you have all invested too much time, energy, and money to call it a loss and walk away without trying to get the firefighter back into their career.

Recommendations

Based on the lessons learned from our case stories, our recommendations are twofold. First, we encourage any firefighter who has been psychologically traumatized on the job to view asking for help as a sign of strength rather than as a sign of weakness. If you have tried to resolve the trauma on your own and have been unsuccessful, it is probably time to seek some outside assistance. Denying that the problem exists or disguising it with drugs or alcohol only makes it more difficult to treat and causes greater disruption to your personal and professional life in the long run.

121

Second, we encourage all departments to do what they do best: expect the worst and be prepared. Don't wait until another good firefighter is lost to traumatic stress. Take a proactive approach, develop a comprehensive plan for preparing for and mitigating traumatic stress among fire personnel, and then use it appropriately. Many firefighters describe joining the fire service as becoming part of a huge family. Be the kind of "family" that they need so that the call that sticks with them is reduced to just one aspect of their career, rather than the thing that ends it.

Appendix A

DSM-IV Diagnostic Criteria for PTSD

(The following has been reprinted with permission by the American Psychiatric Association: Diagnostic and Statistical Manual of Mental Disorder, Fourth Edition, Text Revision. Washington DC: American Psychiatric Association, 2003).

A. The person has been exposed to a traumatic event in which both of the following were present:
- (1) the person experienced, witnessed, or was confronted with an event or events that involved actual or threatened death or serious injury, or a threat to the physical integrity of self or others
- (2) the person's response involves intense fear, helplessness, or horror. **Note:** In children, this may be expressed instead by disorganized or agitated behavior.

B. The traumatic event is persistently reexperienced in one (or more) of the following ways:
- (1) recurrent and intrusive distressing recollections of the event, including images, thoughts, or perceptions. **Note:** In young children, repetitive play may occur in which themes or aspects of the trauma are expressed.
- (2) Recurrent distressing dreams of the event. **Note:** In children, they may be frightening dreams without recognizable content.
- (3) Acting or feeling as if the traumatic event were recurring (includes a sense of reliving the ex-

perience, illusions, hallucinations, and dissociative flashback episodes, including those
that occur on awakening or when intoxicated).
Note: In young children, trauma-specific re-
enactment may occur.

(4) Intense psychological distress at exposure to internal or external cues that symbolize or resemble an aspect of the traumatic event

(5) Physiological reactivity on exposure to internal or
external cues that symbolize or resemble an
aspect of the traumatic event

C. Persistent avoidance of stimuli associated with the
trauma and numbing of general responsiveness (not
present before the trauma), as indicated by three (or
more) of the following:

(1) efforts to avoid thoughts, feelings, or conversations associated with the trauma

(2) efforts to avoid activities, places, or people
that arouse recollections of the trauma

(3) inability to recall an important aspect of the
trauma

(4) markedly diminished interest or participation
in significant activities

(5) feeling of detachment or estrangement from
others

(6) restricted range of affect (e.g., unable to have
loving feelings)

(7) sense of a foreshortened future (e.g., does
not expect to have a career, marriage, children, or a normal life span)

D. Persistent symptoms of increased arousal (not present
before the trauma), as indicated by two (or more) of
the following:

(1)   difficulty falling or staying asleep
(2)   irritability or outbursts of anger
(3)   difficulty concentrating
(4)   hypervigilance
(5)   exaggerated startle response

E. Duration of the disturbance (symptoms in Criteria B, C, and D) is more than 1 month.

F. The disturbance causes clinically significant distress or impairment in social, occupational, or other important areas of functioning.

Specify if:

Acute: If duration of symptoms is less than 3 months
Chronic: If duration of symptoms is 3 months or more.

Specify if:

With Delayed Onset: If onset of symptoms is at least 6 months after the stressor

Appendix B

DSM-IV-TR Diagnostic Criteria for Acute
Stress Disorder
*(The following has been reprinted with permission by
the American Psychiatric Association: Diagnostic and Statistical Manual of Mental Disorder, Fourth Edition, Text
Revision. Washington DC: American Psychiatric Association, 2003).*
A. The person has been exposed to a traumatic event in
which both of the following were present:
  (1) the person experienced, witnessed, or was
  confronted with an event or events that involved actual or threatened death or serious
  injury, or a threat to the physical integrity of
  self or others
  (2) the person's response involved intense fear,
  helplessness, or horror
B. Either while experiencing or after experiencing the
distressing event, the individual has three (or more)
of the following dissociative symptoms:
  (1) a subjective sense of numbing, detachment,
  or absence of emotional responsiveness
  (2) a reduction in awareness of his or her sur-
  roundings (e.g., "being in a daze")
  (3) derealization
  (4) depersonalization
  (5) dissociative amnesia (i.e., inability to recall
  an important aspect of the trauma)
C. The traumatic event is persistently reexperienced in
at least one of the following ways: recurrent images,
thoughts, dreams, illusions, flashback episodes, or a
sense of reliving the experience; or distress on expo-

sures to reminders of the traumatic event.

D. Marked avoidance of stimuli that arouse recollections of the trauma (e.g., thoughts, feelings, conversations, activities, places, people).

E. Marked symptoms of anxiety or increased arousal (e.g., difficulty sleeping, irritability, poor concentration, hypervilance, exaggerated startle response, motor restlessness).

F. The disturbance causes clinically significant distress or impairment in social, occupational, or other important areas of functioning or impairs the individual's ability to pursue some necessary task, such as obtaining necessary assistance or mobilizing personal resources by telling family members about the traumatic experience.

G. The disturbance lasts for a minimum of 2 days and a maximum of 4 weeks and occurs within 4 weeks of the traumatic event.

H. The disturbance is not due to the direct physiological effects of a substance (e.g., a drug of abuse, a medication) or a general medical condition, is not better accounted for by Brief Psychotic Disorder, and is not merely an exacerbation of a preexisting Axis I or Axis II disorder

Appendix C
Resources and Treatment Referrals

Traumatic Stress and PTSD

Anxiety Disorder of America provides reference materials and articles on various mental health issues like anxiety, depression, and PTSD. http://www.adaa.org/AnxietyDisorderInfor/PTSD.cfm

Department of Veterans Affairs (VA) and Department of Defense (DOD) have developed the Post-Traumatic Stress Guideline. http://www.oqp.med.va.gov/cpg/PTSD/PTSD_Base.htm

Expert Consensus Guidelines Treatment of Posttraumatic Stress Disorder is an article which can be accessed at http://www.psychguides.com/gltreatment_of_PTSD.html

Gift From Within is a charitable organization; its website contains articles and resources related to trauma and PTSD for individual and family members. http://www.giftfromwithin.org

International Critical Incident Stress Foundation is a national and international association dedicated to educating and preventing stress relations with the use of peer-support critical incident stress management teams. http://www.ICISF.org

Medication and the Treatment for Combat PTSD, an article by Jonathan Shay, M.D., Ph.D. Staff Psychiatrist, Boston VA Outpatient Clinic, is available at http://www.dr-bob.org/tips/ptsd.html

National Center for Post Traumatic Stress Disorder, developed by the Veterans Administration, articles, further references, and downloadable videos on the disorder. http://www.ncptsd.org/index.html

Posttraumatic Stress Disorder (PTSD) Alliance is a group of professional and advocacy organizations that have joined forces to provide educational resources to individuals diagnosed with PTSD and their loved ones; those at risk for developing PTSD; and medical, healthcare and other frontline professionals. http://www. ptsdalliance.org/home2.html

Rescue-Workers is a website devoted to emergency service workers and PTSD. http://www.rescue-workers.com/1.html

Substance Abuse

Nar-Anon Family Group is a website for friends and family of drug addicts. http://www. soberrecovery. com/links/nar-anon.html

Narcotics Anonymous (NA) is a national and inter national association of recovering drug addicts. http:/ www.na.org

National Council On Alcoholism And Drug Dependence (NCADD) is a resource for the fight against chronic alcoholism and drug addiction. http://www. ncadd.org

Depression and other Mental Health Isses

Depressives Anonymous (DA) is a national group that provides support for people who are suffering from depression.

HealthyPlace is the largest consumer mental health site, providing comprehensive information on psychological disorders and psychiatric medications from both a consumer and expert point of view. http://www. concernedcounseling.com

National Institute of Mental Health web site is a clearinghouse of information on mental health issues. http://www.nimh.nih.gov

U.S. Department of Health and Human Service has as its mission the improvement and expansion of access to quality health care for all. http://www.hrsa.gov

Professional Associations

American College of Physicians web site provides reference material and articles on various mental health issues. http://www.acponline.org/index.html

American Counseling Association website provides information on PTSD and other mental health concerns. The site also provides guidelines on finding a counselor. http://www.counseling.org//AM/Template. Tcfm?Section=Home

American Psychiatric Association is an organization of psychiatrists working together to ensure humane care and effective treatment for all persons with mental disorders, including mental retardation and substance-related disorders. http://www.psych.org/public_info

American Psychological Association Help Center is an online resource for brochures, tips, and articles on the psychological issues that affect one's physical and emotional well-being, as well as information about referrals. http://helping.apa.org

Employee Assistance Program Association, is located at 2101 Wilson Boulevard, Suite 500, Arlington, Virginia, 22201. 703-387-1000. http://www.eapassn.org/public/ pages/index.cfm?pageid=1

International Fellowship of Chaplains, Inc. (IFOC) is a non-profit organization that provides support to government and community organizations. http://www.ifoc.org

International Society for Traumatic Stress Studies (ISTSS) is the world's premier trauma organization, dedicated to trauma treatment, education, research, and prevention. http://www.istss.org

Thought Field Therapy is the professional website for Callahan Techniques Thought Field Therapy. htpp://www.tftrx.com

Treatment Referral Information

American Self-Help Clearinghouse website can assist a person in finding a therapist. http://www.therapistfinder.net/national/selfhelp.html

National Directory of Psychologists lists psychologists throughout the United States. http://psychologyinfo.com/directory/state-links.html

National Mental Health Consumers' Self-Help Clearinghouse is a website to help people find local support or self-help groups. http://www.mhselfhelp.org

Psychology Information Online makes information available about treatment services, specific psychological problems, and ways to locate and select a psychologist to begin treatment. http://www. psychologyinfo. com/consumers/index.html

References

Ahrens, Marty. (2003). *The U.S. fire problem overview report: Leading causes and other patterns and trends.* Retrieved September 22, 2004, from the National Fire Protection Association website: htpp:// www.nfpa.org/assets/files/MbrSecurePDF/Osover.PDF

Al-Naser, F. & Everly, G. (1999). Prevalence of posttraumatic stress disorder among Kuwaiti firefighters. *International Journal of Emergency Mental Health, 1,* 99-101.

American Psychiatric Association. (1987). *Diagnostic and statistical manual of mental disorders* (3rd ed.). Washington, DC: Author.

American Psychiatric Association. (2000). *Diagnostic and statistical manual of mental disorders* (Rev. 4th ed.). Washington, DC: Author.

Bellrose, C. A. & Pilisuk, P. M. (1991). Vocational risk tolerance and perception of occupational hazards. *Basic and Applied Social Psychology, 12,* 303-323.

Bergin, A. E. & Garfield, S. L. (Eds.). (1994). *Handbook of Psychotherapy and Behavior Change* (4th ed.) Provo, UT: Brigham Young University.

Callahan, R. J. & Callahan, J. (2000). *Stop the nightmares of trauma: Thought Field Therapy, the power therapy for the 21st century.* Chapel Hill, NC: Professional Press.

Cardinal, F. (2004). *Sleep deprivation and your health.* Retrieved September 29, 2004, from http://sleepdisorders.about.com/cs/ sleepdeprivation/a/depandhealth.html

Chemtob, C. M., Tolin, D. F., van der Kolk, B. A., & Pitman, R. K. (2000). Eye movement desensitization and reprocessing. In E. B. Foa, T. M. Keane & M. J. Friedman (Eds.), *Effective treatments for PTSD* (pp. 139-154). NY: The Guilford Press.

Dean, G.P., Gow, K., & Shakespeare-Finch, J. (2003). Counting the cost: Psychological distress in career and auxiliary firefighters. *Australasian Journal of Disaster and Trauma Studies, 2003-1,* Retrieved September 19, 2004, from http://www.massey.ac.nz/~trauma/

Dietz, T. (2001). *Scenes of compassion: A responder's guide for dealing with emergency scene emotional crisis.* Ellicott City, MD: Chevron Publishing.

Everly, G. (2000). The role of pastoral crisis intervention in disasters, terrorism, violence, and other community crises. *International Journal of Emergency Mental Health, 2,* 139-141.

Everly, G. S. & Lating, J. M. (2004). *Personality-guided therapy for posttraumatic stress disorder.* Washington, DC: APA.

Everly, G. S. & Mitchell, J.T. (1999). *Critical Incident Stress Management.* Ellicott City, MD: Chevron Publishing.

Everly, G. S. & Mitchell, J.T. (2000). The debriefing "controversy" and crisis intervention: A review of the lexical and substantive issues. *International Journal of Emergency Mental Health, 2,* 211-225.

Federal Emergency Management Association, U.S. Fire Administration. (1991). *FA-100, Stress Management: Model Program for Maintaining Firefighter Well-Being.* Retrieved September 22, 2004, from http://www.usfa.fema.gov/downloads/pdf/publications/ FA-a00.pdf-1185.1KB

References

Flannery, R. B. (2004). *Posttraumatic stress disorder: The victim's guide to healing and recovery* (2ⁿᵈ ed.). Ellicott City, MD: Chevron Publishing.

Flannery, R. B. & Everly, G. S. (2000). Crisis intervention: A review. *International Journal of Emergency Mental Health, 2,* 119-125.

Friedman, M. (2003, May 14). *Posttraumatic Stress Disorder: An overview.* Retrieved September 19, 2003, from http://www.ncptsd.org/facts/general/gs_overview.html

Green, B. & Kaltman, S. (2003). Posttraumatic stress disorder. In R. Simmon (Ed.), *Litigation guidelines for forensic assessment* (2ⁿᵈ ed.). Washington, DC: American Psychiatric Publishing.

Hales, D. & Hales, R. (2004, June 20). Too tough to seek help? *Parade,* 4-6.

Health Effects Plague World Trade Center Rescuers. (2003, September 8). *The Wall Street Journal Online.* Retrieved September 20, 2003 from http://www.wsj.com/article/0,,BT_CO_200309089_0084900.html

Holt, F.X. (1988, November). Assessing risk-taking behaviors in firefighters. *Fire Engineering, 141,* 30-33.

Holborn, R. D. (2002). Motivational factors and personality traits of individuals who decide to enter a career as a firefighter/paramedic (Doctoral dissertation, University of Central Florida, 2002). *Dissertation Abstracts International-B, 63,* 2322.

Horowitz, Mardi. (1997). *Stress response syndromes: PTSD, grief, and adjustment disorders* (3rd ed.) Northvale, NJ: Jason Aronson.

International Association of Fire Fighters. (1992). *2000 death and injury survey.* Washington, DC.: Author.

International Fire Service Training Association. (1992). *Fire Department Occupational Safety* (2nd ed.). Stillwater, OK: Author.

Lee, D. J., Fleming, L. E., Gomez-Marin, O., & LeBlanc, W. (2004). Risk of hospitalization among firefighters: The national health interview survey, 1986-1994. *American Journal of Public Health, 94,* 1938-1939.

Meidi, J. (1970). *Explosive and toxic hazardous materials.* NY: Macmillan Publishing.

Mitchell, J. T. (2004) Characteristics of successful early intervention programs. *International Journal of Emergency Mental Health, 6,* 175-184.

Mitchell, J. & Bray, G. (1990). *Emergency services stress.* Englewood Cliffs, N.J.: Prentice-Hall.

Mitchell, J. T. & Everly, G. S., Jr. (1993). *CISD: An operational manual for the prevention of traumatic stress among emergency services and disaster workers.* Ellicott City, MD: Chevron Publishing.

Neely, K. & Spitzer, W. (1997). A model for a statewide critical incident stress (CIS) debriefing program for emergency services personnel. *Prehospital and Disaster Medicine, 12,* 114-119.

References

North, C., Tivis, L., McMillen, J., Pfefferbaum, B., Cox, J., Spitznagel, E., et al. (2002). Coping, functioning, and adjustment of rescue workers after the Oklahoma City bombing. *Journal of Traumatic Stress, 15,* 173.

Peters, A. & Scott, R. T. (2003, February). *What heroes are made of: Firefighter personality – myth or reality.* Paper presented at the 7th World Congress on Stress, Trauma and Coping, Baltimore, MD.

Schiraldi, G. (2000). *The post-traumatic stress disorder sourcebook.* Lincolnwood, IL: Lowell House.

Simpson, C. & Simpson, D. (1997). *Coping with Post-Traumatic Stress Disorder.* NY: Rosen Publishing.

Taylor, H. (1995, September 22). Post Traumatic Stress Disorder in the fire service. *Fire Engineers Journal, 55,* 22-24.

Tucker, B. (1995, November). Debriefing relieves stress for Buckinghamshire. *Fire, 12.*

United States Fire Administration. (2004). *Heart attack leading cause of death for firefighters* (Release No: 02-193). Retrieved September 25, 2004, from http://www. Usfa.fema.gov/about/media/2002releases/02-193.shtm

Volkmann, P. (2003, November/December). When traumatic events affect the EMS worker: The role of the CISM team. *FireEMS, 53.*

Wagner, D., Heinrichs, M. & Ehlert, U. (1998). Prevalence of symptoms of posttraumatic stress disorder in German professional firefighters. *American Journal of Psychiatry, 155,* 1727-1732.

Warley, R. (2004). Assessment in an EAP setting. *Journal of Employee Assistance, 34,* 7-9.

Williamson, A. M. & Feyer, A. M. (2000). Moderate sleep deprivation produces comprehensive cognitive and motor performance impairments equivalent to legally proscribed levels of alcohol intoxication. *The Journal of Occupational and Environmental Medicine, 57,* 649-655.

Woods, P. (2001, November). Can personal protective clothing influence the risk-taking behavior of firefighters? *Fire Engineers Journal, 61,* 49-52.